Hands-on Culture of
ANCIENT EGYPT

Kate O' Halloran

J. WESTON
WALCH
PUBLISHER
Portland, Maine

Dedication

User's Guide
to
Walch Reproducible Books

As part of our general effort to provide educational materials which are as practical and economical as possible, we have designated this publication a "reproducible book." The designation means that purchase of the book includes purchase of the right to limited reproduction of all pages on which this symbol appears:

Here is the basic Walch policy: We grant to individual purchasers of this book the right to make sufficient copies of reproducible pages for use by all students of a single teacher. This permission is limited to a single teacher, and does not apply to entire schools or school systems, so institutions purchasing the book should pass the permission on to a single teacher. Copying of the book or its parts for resale is prohibited.

Any questions regarding this policy or requests to purchase further reproduction rights should be addressed to:

Permissions Editor
J. Weston Walch, Publisher
321 Valley Street • P. O. Box 658
Portland, Maine 04104-0658

1   2   3   4   5   6   7   8   9   10

ISBN 0-8251-3088-3

Contents

How to Use This Book

This book, like the others in the *Hands-on Culture* series by J. Weston Walch, Publisher, has been designed to help middle school teachers integrate the study of a culture into the curriculum. Textbooks can teach students about the history and geography of an area, but to gain any real understanding, students must also be exposed to the art and traditions of a culture.

Hands-on Culture of Ancient Egypt provides 15 ready-to-use activities to help you do just that. Through the projects in this book, students will be exposed to the economy, writing, mathematics, religion, art, and literature of ancient Egypt.

Most of the projects in this book work well either as individual projects or as group activities. As students deal with such unfamiliar material as mathematics using Egyptian symbols, they may find it less intimidating to work together to find solutions.

By their nature, all of these projects are interdisciplinary. All are appropriate for a social studies class. Most are appropriate for an art class. Some activities are also appropriate for other subject areas; the correlation chart on page *vi* presents these links. Some activities could be done in several different classes. The Drama: Festival of Osiris activity on page 40 and the Early Irrigation: The Shaduf activity on page 9 are examples of this type of activity. For the Festival of Osiris, the background could be given in a social studies class, acts and scenes could be explained and the play actually written in English class, and the masks could be made in art class. For the shaduf activity, the background could be given in social studies, the discussion of the lever could be given in science class, and the shaduf could be made in art class.

Of course, some elements of Egyptian history and culture are not included in this book. Excellent activities on topics like building the pyramids and making sarcophagi are easily available in other resources. We have attempted here to provide integrated activities and information on some of the most central elements of the culture: the economy, the land, communication, religion, literature, science, and the afterlife.

If you are teaching about ancient Egypt as part of an interdiscplinary team, each teacher can teach the activities appropriate to his or her domain. All the projects have been structured so that the teacher presenting the activity does not need to know either the historical context for an activity or the procedure for doing the project. Full background details are provided where needed. You can share some or all of this information with students if you wish, but it is not necessary for student completion of the project. The step-by-step student instructions for the activities should need no further explanation.

To help demonstrate the process, you may find it helpful to keep one or two examples of student work for each activity. The next time you present the activity, show the student work as models. When dealing with unfamiliar material, it can help if students have a general idea of what is expected of them.

I hope that you—and your students—enjoy this book, and that it helps deepen your students' understanding and appreciation of ancient Egypt.

Subject Area Correlation

	MATH	SCIENCE	LANGUAGE ARTS	ART	SOCIAL STUDIES
Trade and Barter: How Many Ducks for a Goat?	x			x	x
Figure Painting: Draw like an Egyptian				x	x
Early Irrigation: The Shaduf		x		x	x
Hieroglyphics: Picture Writing			x	x	x
Egyptian Math: Reading Symbols	x				x
Egyptian Math: Multiplication and Division	x				x
Medicine and Magic: Amulets		x		x	x
Justice System: The Eloquent Peasant			x		x
Religion of Egypt: Hundreds of Gods				x	x
Drama: The Festival of Osiris			x	x	x
Playing Games in Ancient Egypt	x			x	x
Packing for the Afterlife				x	x
Making a Mummy		x		x	x
Model Workers				x	x
The Game of the Afterlife				x	x

Trade and Barter:
How Many Ducks for a Goat?

OBJECTIVES

Social Studies
- Students will simulate an economy based on barter.

Math
- Students will practice conversion concepts with trade items.

Art
- Students will create a visual symbol for a concrete object.

MATERIALS

Trade and Barter handout
Items to Barter handout
colored photocopy paper
optional: index cards, drawing supplies

BACKGROUND

Money was not used in Egypt until Grecian times, around 500 B.C. Until then, all goods and services were exchanged by bartering. To make everyday marketing easier, traders used a balance scale and weights known as *deben* to work out the value of goods.

The markets of small towns in Egypt were filled with locally grown produce. In large towns, goods from many lands were available. Egypt traded with many other areas in Africa, the Near East, and the Mediterranean. Imports included perfumes from Punt (possibly present-day Somalia), silver from Syria, precious stones from Ethiopia, cedar from Lebanon, iron from Palestine, gold and copper from Nubia, and olive oil from Greece.

The symbols on the Items to Barter handout are the hieroglyphics for the Egyptian words.

PREPARATION

Make copies of the Items to Barter handout on two different colors of paper and cut them apart. There are 15 items on the handout. You will need one item in each color for each student. Otherwise students will be unable to complete their trade by finding another student with the same item.

PROCEDURE

1. Distribute the Trade and Barter handout and discuss it with students.

2. Place the slips in two piles, according to color, and designate one as the To Barter pile and the other as the To Buy pile.

3. Tell students to choose one card from each pile, and explain that they have to trade one and acquire the other.

4. If you wish, have students begin the activity by drawing the object they have to offer in trade on an index card. Since the card is a symbol, not the actual item, the drawing should simplify the item to its essential features. Encourage students to include the hieroglyphics for the item.

5. Tell students that you have appointed yourself official market attendant, and you will intervene in any disputes.

6. Have students proceed as directed on the handout, trying to trade the item they have for the item they need.

7. When all students have completed their trades—or after a prearranged time limit—ask students what they thought of the process. How many trades, on average, did students need to make to acquire the desired item? What do they think are the advantages of a barter system? the disadvantages?

VARIATION

To simplify the activity, choose four or five of the items on the Items to Barter sheet and copy only those items.

EXTENSION ACTIVITIES

- Most of the items on the Items to Barter page were important to the ancient Egyptians. Have students find out why the items they acquired were important.

- Egypt traded with other countries, exporting corn, lentils, papyrus, and linen. What additional complications would arise when bartering with another country?

- Direct students to research Egyptian marketplaces and create a diorama.

ASSESSMENT

Based on this experience, ask students to list the advantages and disadvantages of bartering as a way of distributing goods.

Trade and Barter:
How Many Ducks for a Goat?

In early Egypt, as in other early societies, people were very self-sufficient. Each family provided its own food, shelter, and clothing. Then, as Egyptian civilization developed, people started to specialize. Some people gave all of their attention to growing food. Others became craftspersons. A town might have a weaver to make fabric, a potter for dishes, a shoemaker for sandals. Then if the potter and weaver needed sandals, they went to the shoemaker instead of making their own sandals.

That probably sounds to you pretty much like the way people buy things today. But one major difference is that the ancient Egyptians had no money. The idea of money hadn't been developed yet. So the Egyptians used a system called **barter**, where they traded one thing for another.

Wages in ancient Egypt were paid in food and clothing. So if you wanted a pair of sandals, you needed to have something the sandalmaker wanted that was worth about the same as a pair of sandals. You would take your item to the open-air market, where stalls were set out along the street, and try to trade for the item you wanted. There was often a lot of arguing about the value of the things being traded. An official market attendant was there to keep order.

 In this activity, you will play the part of an ancient Egyptian at the market. Choose two slips—one from the To Barter pile and one from the To Buy pile. The item named on the To Barter slip is the item you have with you when you arrive at the market. The item on the To Buy slip is the item you need to get. If you're lucky, the person with the item you want will want the item you have. Otherwise, you may need to make several trades before you get the thing you need. To make your bartering easier, we'll say that all the items have the same value. See how many trades it takes you to get the item you need.

When you make a trade, exchange your To Barter card for the other person's To Barter card. Your trade is completed when your To Barter and To Buy cards list the same item.

When you have successfully completed your trade, return to your seat and place both the To Buy and To Barter cards face up on your desk.

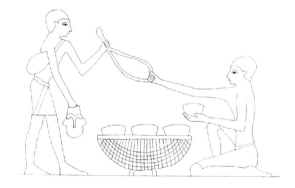

Items to Barter

necklace	ivory	tambourine

alabaster	bread	papyrus

arrow	eye paint	grain

rope	sandals	scarab

cat	mirror	ointment

Figure Painting:
Draw like an Egyptian

OBJECTIVES

Social Studies

- Students will see how belief systems can affect other aspects of a culture.
- Students will understand the criteria used in creating Egyptian art.
- Students will express an aspect of their daily lives using the criteria of another culture.
- Students will see that information about a culture is not limited to written sources.

Art

- Students will understand the context and purpose of figure drawing in ancient Egypt.
- Students will compare different purposes for creating works of art.

MATERIALS

Figure Painting: Draw like an Egyptian handout
paper, pencils, other drawing materials
paints or markers
optional: slides or reproductions of Egyptian figure paintings

BACKGROUND

To modern Western eyes, the ancient Egyptian approach to drawing humans looks strange, but our art would look just as odd to them. That's because the two societies had very different reasons for making art. When Westerners first began studying Egyptian art, they tended to dismiss it as rigid and primitive. They felt the paintings showed no spontaneity, no use of perspective, and no modeling with color. Only when the purposes of Egyptian art became clear could the art be appreciated for what it was, rather than criticized for what it was not.

In the modern West, art is an end to itself. It exists only to be art. In ancient Egypt, art was primarily a way to translate religious experience into visual form. All art was designed to reflect the Egyptian idea of life, both in this world and in the afterlife.

Because so much Egyptian art was designed to be of use in the afterlife, it had to be as clear as possible. It would be terrible to go through eternity with no right hand just because a tomb drawing wasn't clear! For this reason, Egyptian art developed a set of rules for representing the parts of the body in the most recognizable way. Rather than a single view of the body, the Egyptian representation is a composite image combining several different views.

5

You might wish to tell students about the one brief break in the Egyptian artistic tradition. The eighteenth-dynasty pharaoh Akhenaten broke away from the traditional polytheistic religion and called for the worship of a single sun-god, Aten. During the 17 years of Akhenaten's reign, 1379–1363 B.C., a new artistic style was seen. Figures were shown as more relaxed and lifelike. Some were even allowed to be shown with flaws. However, after Akhenaten's death, Egyptian society—and art—quickly returned to the traditional ways.

Painters in ancient Egypt were not seen as artists in the way we view artists today. They were craftspersons, who often worked as part of a team to paint a wall. First came the mason, who smoothed the wall and covered it in a thin layer of plaster. Then this white surface was marked with a grid of squares by dipping a length of string in red paint and holding the string taut against the wall. A preparatory sketch was done on a small piece of stone or wood, then a grid of lines was drawn over this sketch. To transfer the small drawing to the wall, the artist worked on one square at a time, exactly copying the lines shown in the small square on the sketch onto the corresponding large square on the wall.

At this point, a stonemason might be employed to cut away the background, leaving the figures in relief, or the whole surface might be left flat. In either case, the final step was coloring in the figures with a brush made from fibrous reeds; the background was left blank. The color was applied in a flat, even wash, with no attempt to show three dimensions through the use of shading.

PROCEDURE

1. Distribute the handout and discuss it with students. If you wish, show slides or reproductions that illustrate the rules of Egyptian figure painting.

2. Have students proceed as directed on the handout.

ASSESSMENT

Did students produce drawings that show a contemporary scene according to the rules of ancient Egyptian art (no perspective; heads in profile; eyes facing forward; chests and shoulders forward; arms, waist, hips, legs facing sideways; both hands—with fingers—shown; left leg in front of right, and as much as possible of both legs shown)?

EXTENSION ACTIVITY

Explain to students the Egyptian method of enlarging by squares. Direct them to draw an even grid of squares over one of the figures in the illustration on the student handout and enlarge the drawing using this method.

Figure Painting:
Draw like an Egyptian

A lot of what we know about ancient Egyptians comes from their art. The walls of tombs were decorated with scenes of everyday life. We see pictures of people working in the fields, baking, fishing, boating, playing, and relaxing with family and friends.

If you have seen reproductions of Egyptian paintings, you have probably noticed that people are shown at a strange angle. Their heads are always shown in profile, their shoulders face forward, and their chests, waists, and legs are in profile. If you try to stand in this position, you will realize that the Egyptians weren't painting people the way they really looked. But it's obvious that these ancient artists were able to draw very well. Why did they draw people in a way that seems so strange to us?

In fact, our art would seem just as odd to the ancient Egyptians as theirs seems to us. That's because artists today and in ancient Egypt had very different purposes in mind. Tomb paintings show ideal versions of people—the way people wanted to look in their new, eternal life. Physical problems were rarely shown. Egyptian artists even avoided showing any emotion on the faces of their paintings.

Ancient Egyptian artists were not trying to draw what they saw but what they knew was there. When they drew figures of people on the walls of tombs, they expected their drawings to come to life in the land of Osiris, the life after death. It was important to show every part of the body as clearly as possible. If an arm or a leg in tomb artwork could not be seen clearly, the person might not be able to use that arm or leg in the afterlife.

(continued)

Figure Painting:
Draw like an Egyptian *(continued)*

To make sure tomb paintings were as complete and correct as possible, rules for art developed. In a group of people, an important person would be drawn much larger than other people. Heads were shown in profile, but the eyes looked as if they were seen from the front. The shoulders and chest were seen from the front. The waist and legs were in profile. Both arms were clearly shown, as well as the fingers on each hand. The left leg was usually in front of the right one, and as much as possible was shown of both legs.

Another aspect of Egyptian art that may seem strange to Western eyes is its flatness. Since the Middle Ages, Western artists have tried to show what they really see. This often means trying to make a flat surface look as if it has three dimensions. Artists use perspective and shading to suggest roundness. To Egyptian artists, this was not important. Objects and people were drawn very simply, with no attempt to use perspective. Surfaces were covered with flat, even color. Men are usually shown with reddish-brown skin. Women's skin is a lighter, yellowish tone.

The paints used by Egyptian artists were made by crushing rocks and minerals, then mixing the powder with egg white and gum arabic, a sticky plant extract. Malachite and lapis lazuli, two semiprecious stones, were used to make green and blue pigments. Iron oxide was used for red. Yellow was made from ochre. Gypsum and calcium carbonate were used to make white, and black was made from soot and crushed charcoal. Many of the paintings made using these colors appear as fresh and brilliant today as when they were first painted thousands of years ago.

Although people were drawn in such stiff, unnatural poses, they were often shown doing everyday things. Think of some of the things you do every day, or that you like to do. Try drawing an activity you like in the ancient Egyptian style. Draw a person by following the rules described above: head sideways, eyes front, chest and shoulders front, legs, hips, and arms sideways. Show the details of the activity clearly, but don't try to use perspective—Egyptian artists showed objects stacked on top of each other, or as if they were seen from above. Then fill in the outlines of your drawing with smooth, flat colors, leaving the background blank.

Hands-on Culture of Ancient Egypt

Early Irrigation: The Shaduf

OBJECTIVES

Social Studies

- Students will understand how civilization began in the Nile Valley.
- Students will see how early Egyptians used technology to shape the environment.

Science

- Students will understand how rivers carry and deposit sediment.
- Students will see an early example of the use of a simple machine, the lever.
- Students will understand how human action can affect the environment.
- Students will learn the early history of irrigation.

Art

- Students will make a working model of a shaduf.

MATERIALS

Early Irrigation: The Shaduf handout
For each shaduf:
wood, sticks, or rigid tubing in the following lengths:
     two 8" lengths
     one 6" length
     one 16" length
piece of polyurethane or clay-covered board 6" × 6" to use as base
small container, about 2" in diameter
small objects (bolts, nuts, ball bearings) to use as weights
string
tape

BACKGROUND

The lever is one of the six simple machines—tools with only a few parts. These machines can make work easier in a variety of ways. The main advantage of using a lever is that it increases the force you exert on an object to move it.

Levers consist of three parts: an effort arm, a resistance arm, and a fulcrum, or balance point. In the shaduf, the fulcrum is between the effort arm and the resistance arm.

The shaduf is known to have been developed by 1500 B.C.E., although it may well have been developed before then. This simple machine is still in use today in many parts of the world.

PROCEDURE

1. Distribute the handout to students, and discuss it with them.

2. If you wish, you can demonstrate the principle of the lever with a book, a ruler, and a small object like a cork. Use the cork as the fulcrum and the ruler as a lever to lift the book.

3. Demonstrate for students the first steps in building the shaduf by setting the uprights and the crosspiece.

4. Have students proceed as directed on the handout.

EXTENSION ACTIVITY

Explain to students the concept of the mechanical advantage, or M.A., of a machine. The M.A. is a value that tells how many times a machine increases the force applied. The M.A. of a lever can be calculated by dividing the length of the effort arm by the length of the resistance arm. In a 10-foot-long seesaw, where the effort arm and the resistance arm are both 5 feet long, this equation reads as 5/5, or 1. Using a lever with an M.A. of 1, a person could lift a weight equal to his or her own weight, but no more. However, if the effort arm is 4 feet long and the resistance arm is 2 feet long, the equation reads 4/2, or 2. This means that the lever exerts twice as much force as the person using it exerts. Based on their experience with shifting the balance point of the shaduf, ask students to say which arm of the shaduf is the resistance arm and which is the effort arm. What is the M.A. of each shaduf?

BONUS QUESTION

Some of the results were anticipated, but some were surprising. Results include:

- Because of the dam, the Nile no longer floods. Without the rich silt deposited by the river during flood seasons, farmers must now rely heavily on fertilizers.
- A fertile strip of land above the dam in Nubia was flooded and is now underneath Lake Nasser.
- Some ancient monuments have been covered by water. Others were moved, at great expense, to save them.
- The mud carried by the Nile is now being caught by the dam and is gradually choking the reservoir.
- Now that the river is no longer scoured by the annual floods, water snails are gradually working their way upstream. These snails spread bilharzia, a parasite that affects people working in irrigated lands.

ASSESSMENT

Did students understand the principle of the lever and use it to make a working model of a shaduf?

Early Irrigation: The Shaduf

"Hail to thee, O Nile, that issues from the earth and comes to keep Egypt alive."

The unknown Egyptian who wrote this line about 4,000 years ago wasn't exaggerating. The Nile River really did keep Egypt alive. Egypt gets very little rain. Deserts lie to the east and west of the Nile Valley. Without the river, there would be no water to drink and no way of growing food.

For most of the year, the Nile winds quietly along for 4,000 miles (6,400 km) from its source until it reaches the sea. But every June, seasonal winds cause steady rains in Ethiopia, far to the south of Egypt. The heavy rain causes the river to rise. It carries away soil and fine sediment, or silt, in the swift water. As the Nile flows north toward the Mediterranean, the river overflows its banks.

When the floodwaters go down, they leave a layer of fine silt on the land on either side of the river. This silt is very fertile, and crops grow well in the soil left by the flood. Beyond the floodplain, where the waters do not reach, the ground is barren desert.

Thousands of years ago, people realized that it was easy to grow food along the banks of the Nile River. The river was full of fish. The reeds along its banks were a good place to hunt birds. And the river could be relied on to flood the fields every year and deposit fresh soil so that crops would grow. As people settled along the river, a powerful civilization arose, with the Nile River at its center.

A lot of the science of ancient Egypt was developed to predict and direct the waters of the Nile floods. The Egyptians developed a calendar to time the flood. They developed mathematical formulas to measure it and to survey the fields every year after the water went down. And to take advantage of the water even when it wasn't flooding, they developed a system of irrigation.

By 5000 B.C.E., farmers had started to control the floodwaters of the Nile. They built a network of canals and dikes. When the water was high, it would flow into the canals and irrigate the fields. The dikes were used to control the water flow. When the river was at its normal level, the water was lower than the canals. Laborers used buckets to scoop water out of the river and pour it into the canals.

Then someone developed a simple machine to make it easier to move water. This machine was called the ***shaduf***. Machines make work easier by transferring force. Some machines, like the lever, do this by multiplying the force a person uses to get a job done. The shaduf is a type of lever. It makes work easier by increasing the force you use to move something.

Essentially, a lever is a long bar with a balance point, or fulcrum, that allows it to pivot. For example, a seesaw is a kind of lever. The seat is the lever arm, and the base is the balance point, or fulcrum. If you sit on one end of the seesaw, you can easily lift a weight at the other end. The lever (seesaw) increases the force you exert.

(continued)

Early Irrigation: The Shaduf *(continued)*

In a shaduf, a weight is attached to one end of the lever arm. A bucket is attached to the other end so that it hangs over the river. To use the shaduf, the farmer pulls down on the bucket end of the lever until the bucket reaches the water. When the bucket is full, the farmer gently releases the pressure. The weight at the other end of the lever sinks to the ground and lifts the bucket.

 Using this description and the illustration below, make your own working model of a shaduf. You should begin by fixing the two 8-inch uprights into the base about 4 inches apart. Then attach the 6-inch crosspiece across the top of the two 8-inch pieces. Next, use string to attach the container to one end of the 16-inch arm of the shaduf. The container should hang freely from the end of the shaduf. Attach the weight to the other end of the shaduf arm. Balance the shaduf arm on the crosspiece.

To test your shaduf, raise the weighted end of the arm: the container should be lowered to base level. Place a few small items in the container. Release the weighted end of the shaduf. As the weight sinks to the ground, it should gently raise the container.

Experiment with balancing the lever at different points on the support (fulcrum) until you get the most effective shaduf. If you want, you can experiment with the amount of weight on the end of the shaduf. Which changes make the shaduf easier to use? Which make it harder to use?

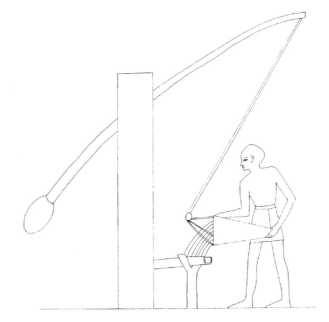

Bonus Question

In 1968, the Nile River was dammed at Aswan. What effects do you think this might have had on farming between the dam and the mouth of the river? What effects might the dam have had on other aspects of life in Egypt?

Hieroglyphics: Picture Writing

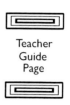

OBJECTIVES

Social Studies

- Students will understand how the Egyptian writing system developed.
- Students will see that different cultures develop different ways to communicate.

Language Arts

- Students will see the difference between an alphabetic and a glyph system of writing.

Art

- Students will practice using symbols to express ideas.

MATERIALS

Hieroglyphics: Picture Writing handout
paper, writing utensils

BACKGROUND

The word *hieroglyph* actually comes from the Greek and means "sacred writing in stone." For centuries after the close of the Egyptian empire, hieroglyphics were a mystery that no one could read. Then in 1822 Jean François Champollion, a brilliant young French linguist, discovered the key to reading the Rosetta Stone, a tablet with writing in hieroglyphics, demotic, and Greek. Hieroglyphic writing could again be deciphered.

The hieroglyphic system uses a total of about 700 signs, 23 of them alphabetic. Most of the rest represent combinations of sounds, while some signs stand for whole words. Most signs are based on things commonly found in ancient Egypt such as people, animals, plants, and objects.

Hieroglyphic writing was only one of three scripts used to write Egyptian, although it was the first one developed. The second script, called *hieratic*, was essentially a joined, cursive version of hieroglyphics, much quicker to write than hieroglyphics, as our cursive script is faster to write than block printing. The third script, *demotic*, which developed around the seventh century B.C.E., was even more abbreviated than the hieratic script. After hieratic developed, hieroglyphics were used mainly for royal texts and for religious texts to be carved in stone. For most other purposes, the faster hieratic script was used.

Hieroglyphic signs could be read in several different directions: left to right, right to left, or top to bottom. To tell which direction a group of signs should be read in, check to see which way the human and animal signs are facing. Since they always face toward the beginning of the line, you should read toward their faces.

With so many symbols, most people did not learn how to read and write. Letters, records, and literature were generally written by scribes.

Becoming a scribe was a long, slow process. Students in scribe school were all boys; some daughters of well-off families were taught to write by tutors, but most girls received no formal education at all. To become scribes, boys started school at an early age and studied for about 10 years. They began their training by learning to write signs on pieces of stone and pottery. Papyrus, which was expensive to make, was reserved until students were more experienced.

Since the work done by scribes was very varied, students learned more than just how to read and write. They also had lessons in astronomy, astrology, mathematics, and science.

Although becoming a scribe was slow and difficult, it was also one of the few ways a boy could change his position in life. Generally, a son was trained to follow his father's profession. A potter's son became a potter, a carpenter's son became a carpenter. But anyone with the ability and diligence could become a scribe and find a broad range of opportunities available. The wide variety of records kept by scribes are an invaluable resource for scholars who wish to know about life in ancient Egypt.

PROCEDURE

1. Distribute the handout and discuss it with students.

2. Divide students into pairs.

3. Have students proceed as directed on the handout.

ASSESSMENT

Were students able to decipher each other's hieroglyph messages?

EXTENSION ACTIVITY

Hieroglyphics can be used as the basis for a number of different activities, including writing the student's name within an oval cartouche, like the names of pharaohs of ancient Egypt; creating a clay cylinder seal of a student's name; or carving a relief in plaster using hieroglyphic signs.

Hieroglyphics: Picture Writing

Here are two sentences written in English. Can you read them? If you can, then you should understand how ancient Egyptians read hieroglyphic writing.

Th-y sw-m -w-y v-ry sw-ftly.

Hieroglyphics are the pictures ancient Egyptians used for writing important information—like the words of the king, or religious texts. When this writing system began, about 6,000 years ago, every picture stood for the word it showed. In the picture sentence above, the stands for the word *fish*.

That system works well if you only write about things you can show clearly with a picture, but how do you write about ideas, like "friendship" or "cousin"? Over time, Egyptian writers changed the way they used some signs. Instead of standing for the original word, signs were used to stand for a word that sounded like the original word, but meant something different. In the sentence above, the and the  are being used that way. Using some signs for sounds and some for meaning made it easier to write about abstract ideas, things that were hard to draw.

Gradually, a system developed in which some signs stood for a single sound, the way the letters of our alphabet stand for a single sound. Some stood for a syllable, or a combination of sounds. And some still stood for the thing they showed. Altogether, the system used about 700 different signs.

One curious thing about the signs that stood for sounds was that they only showed the consonant sounds, not the vowels. (Westerners have added vowels—usually the letter *e*—to a lot of Egyptian words, just to make it possible for us to pronounce them. But we really don't know what the words sounded like in ancient Egypt.) Look at the second sentence at the top of the page. All the vowels have been taken out of the words. Still, they're not that hard to figure out. The only one that might be confusing is **sw-m**. You can't tell whether it means *swim* or *swam*, but the meanings of both of these words are pretty close to each other. Other words could be harder to figure out. For example, the word **c-t** could be *cat*, *cot*, or *cut*, depending on what the missing vowel was.

To solve this problem, the Egyptians added another kind of sign to the sound signs and sense signs. These signs were called *determinatives*. They helped the reader determine which word was being used. With **c-t**, you might show you meant a *cat* by adding a drawing of an animal: c-t 🐆 . You might show a *cot* by using a drawing of a piece of furniture: c-t ▬ . And for *cut*, you might show a knife: c-t ➤ . None of the drawings would need to show exactly

(continued)

       Hands-on Culture of Ancient Egypt

Hieroglyphics: Picture Writing *(continued)*

the word you meant. They would just show the area of meaning: an animal, a piece of furniture, something sharp. The drawings would make it easier for your reader to tell which word you meant.

That's the way the Egyptians used determinative signs. To show that a word referred to a man, they drew a little 🧎 after it. To show it was a woman, they used 👤. Verbs that involved movement showed a pair of legs walking: ∧. Abstract ideas—ideas that really couldn't be shown with a picture—were followed by a roll of papyrus: ⌿ . None of these determinative signs were pronounced. They were only used when the word was written, to make the meaning clear.

Below and on the following page are three groups of Egyptian hieroglyph signs. The first group shows the signs that stand for single sounds, like our alphabet. There are one or two vowel sounds, but most of the vowels are left out. The second group shows some sense signs, signs that stand for a whole word. The third group shows some of the determinative signs, signs that explain the area of meaning for a word.

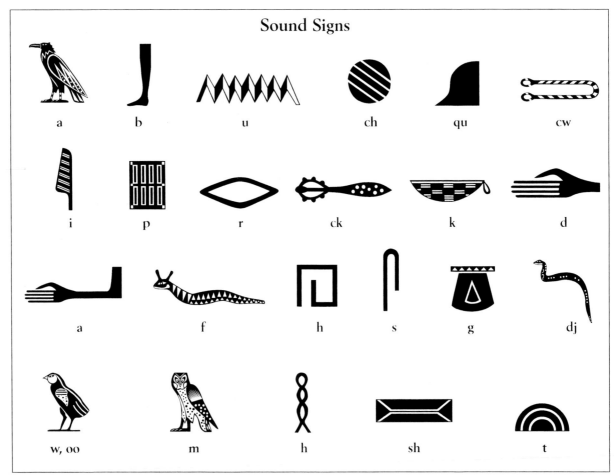

Sound Signs

a	b	u	ch	qu	cw
i	p	r	ck	k	d
a	f	h	s	g	dj
w, oo	m	h	sh	t	

(continued)

Hieroglyphics: Picture Writing *(continued)*

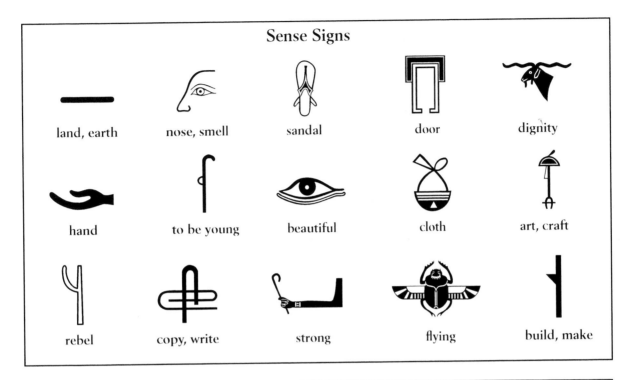

Sense Signs

land, earth	nose, smell	sandal	door	dignity
hand	to be young	beautiful	cloth	art, craft
rebel	copy, write	strong	flying	build, make

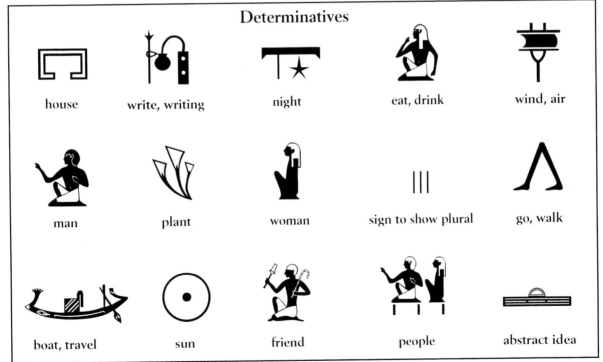

Determinatives

house	write, writing	night	eat, drink	wind, air
man	plant	woman	sign to show plural	go, walk
boat, travel	sun	friend	people	abstract idea

(continued)

    17   *Hands-on Culture of Ancient Egypt*

Hieroglyphics: Picture Writing *(continued)*

 Try to write your name using hieroglyphics. Remember, most vowel sounds weren't written out, and you should use a determinative sign at the end of your name.

_____

Now, on the back of this sheet, try writing an English sentence using hieroglyphics. Some words may be hard to form, because every language has some unique sounds. English uses some sounds that Egyptian didn't have, and some Egyptian sounds aren't used in English. Do your best to reproduce English sounds with the Egyptian signs, leaving out the vowels. Use determinatives wherever they seem appropriate.

When you have finished, exchange papers with a partner. Try to read the sentence you have been given. Which did you find easier, translating English sounds into Egyptian signs, or figuring out the English from the hieroglyphics?

Be glad you only needed to learn 26 signs to write English, not 700!

Some English words came originally from Egyptian words. The word *desert* comes from the Egyptian word *dshrt,* referring to the dry land outside the floodplain of the Nile. And the Egyptian word for a container, *saak,* has become our word *sack.*

Hands-on Culture of Ancient Egypt

Egyptian Math:
Reading Symbols

OBJECTIVES

Social Studies
- Students will see that different cultures develop different responses to the same need.

Math
- Students will learn about the number symbols used in ancient Egypt.

MATERIALS

Egyptian Math: Reading Symbols handout
paper
pencils

BACKGROUND

Egyptian math probably first developed as part of the ongoing effort to track and control the flooding of the Nile. As mathematical knowledge progressed, it was used to deal with problems like land surveying and tax assessment. Egyptian mathematicians used concepts like fractions and square roots and calculated area and volume.

PROCEDURE

1. Divide students into pairs.

2. Distribute the handout and discuss it with students.

3. Practice writing Indo-Arabic numbers in hieroglyphics, and vice versa.

4. Have students proceed as directed on the handout.

ANSWERS

1. 1,204

2. 1,010,003

3. 37

4. ∩∩∩∩ |||||
   ∩∩∩ ||||

5. @∩∩|||

6. ⌒ @@@@@
      @@@@ ||

7. ⚡ @@@@ ∩∩
      @@@ ∩

The Great Pyramid

The Great Pyramid at Giza was built about [4,000] years ago. As many as [10,000] laborers worked on it during the [23] years it took to complete. The pyramid is made of about [2,000,000] blocks of stone, each one weighing over [2] tons. Some weighed much more. The whole pyramid contains nearly [6,000,000] tons of stone! Some of the granite for the pyramid was cut at Aswan, about [500] miles away, and transported to Giza in barges on the Nile. The completed pyramid, which is [486] feet ([146] meters) high, covers an area of more than [2,556] square feet, or [230] square meters.

ASSESSMENT

Were students able to read and write hieroglyphic numbers?

EXTENSION ACTIVITY

Explain to students that the ancient Egyptian processes for adding and subtracting numbers were very much the same as those we use today, just with different symbols. Model some addition and subtraction problems on the board, then direct students to prepare two addition and two subtraction problems each. Either have each student trade papers with a partner and solve the partner's problems, or choose some problems to put on the board and ask the whole class to solve them. In these problems, the numbers are written as they were in ancient Egypt, from right to left instead of left to right. To make the material more accessible for your students, you may wish to transpose the symbols to read from left to right.

Some sample problems:

Egyptian Math: Reading Symbols

Like many other developments in Egypt, Egyptian mathematics probably began with the Nile River.

As early as 3000 B.C.E., Egyptians were able to predict how high the Nile flood would be. They cut gauges, called *nilometers*, into the rock sides of the river channel at the southern end of Egypt. As the river rose, observers checked to see how high it reached on the gauge. They kept track of which marks the river reached in earlier years and what the flood had been like in those years.

The Egyptians then used those records to make predictions. They knew that if the river reached a high mark on the nilometer, the flood would be disastrously high. If it reached a low mark, the flood would be so low that the harvest would be poor. This knowledge let the Egyptians decide in advance how much landowners should be taxed each year and whether they would have plenty of grain or would need to ration it.

Before they could do all this, they needed to be able to measure, count, and keep records. They developed a system of numbers using different symbols, like hieroglyphics. Like the system we use today, the Egyptian system was based on 10. The numbers from 1 to 9 were written with short vertical lines. Each multiple of 10 had its own special mark.

1	|	6	||| / |||	100	@
2	||	7	|||| / |||	1,000	⚘
3	|||	8	|||| / ||||	10,000	◗
4	||||	9	||||| / ||||	100,000	𓅐
5	||| / ||	10	∩	1,000,000	𓀀

Because there was a different symbol for every multiple of 10, the Egyptians didn't use place value. In our system, the value of a number depends on its position relative to zero. We use the same symbol whether the number has a value in the tens or in the thousands. Using the ancient Egyptian system, it didn't matter what order you wrote the numbers in. The symbols always had the same meaning. Because of this, the symbols for some numbers often appear stacked on top of each other.

23 ∩∩||| 3,234 ⚘⚘⚘ @@ ∩∩∩||||

107 @|||| / ||| 11,247 ◗ ⚘ @@ ∩∩|||| / ∩∩|||

(continued)

Egyptian Math: Reading Symbols (continued)

Try writing these Egyptian numbers in modern Indo-Arabic numerals.

1. 𓏤 @@ |||| _____

2. 𓁨 𓆼 ||| _____

3. ∩∩∩ ||||/||| _____

Now write these Indo-Arabic numbers in Egyptian numerals.

4. 79 _____

5. 123 _____

6. 10,902 _____

7. 1,000,730 _____

Below is some information about the Great Pyramid of Cheops (Khufu), one of the seven wonders of the ancient world. The words are written in English, but all the numbers are written in Egyptian numerals. Can you read what it says?

The Great Pyramid at Giza was built about 𓏴𓏴𓏴𓏴 years ago. As many as 𓆼 laborers worked on it during the ∩∩ ||| years it took to complete. The pyramid is made of about 𓁨 𓁨 blocks of stone, each one weighing over || tons. Some weighed much more. The whole pyramid contains nearly 𓁨𓁨𓁨 𓁨𓁨𓁨 tons of stone! Some of the granite for the pyramid was cut at Aswan, about @@@ @@ miles away, and transported to Giza in barges on the Nile. The completed pyramid, which is @@ ∩∩∩∩ ||| / @@ ∩∩∩∩ ||| feet (@ ∩∩ ||| / ∩∩ ||| meters) high, covers an area of more than 𓏤𓏤 @@@ ∩∩∩ ||| / @@ ∩∩ ||| square feet, or @@ ∩∩∩ square meters.

Write a paragraph of your own about ancient Egypt that uses numbers. Use Egyptian symbols to write the numerals. Trade papers with a partner, and see if you can read the whole paragraph.

Egyptian Math:
Multiplication and Division

OBJECTIVES

Social Studies

• Students will have some understanding of the extent and limitations of Egyptian developments in mathematics.

Math

• Students will learn about the Egyptian method of calculating.

MATERIALS

Egyptian Math: Multiplication and Division handout
paper
pencils

BACKGROUND

Although the ancient Egyptians were obviously adept and accurate at measuring and tallying, they did not pursue mathematics in the abstract. The Egyptian approach to mathematics was purely practical. They developed what they needed and apparently did not explore further.

Much of Egyptian mathematics is based on the 2-times table. Their method of multiplication calls for successive doubling of the numbers to be multiplied. To save time, tables of useful multiplications were available.

PROCEDURE

1. Distribute the handout and discuss it with students.

2. Divide students into pairs.

3. Have students proceed as directed on the handout.

ASSESSMENT

Were students able to prepare and solve problems using the Egyptian method?

EXTENSION

Egyptian multiplication uses the distributive property of multiplication over addition. Ask students how they would write the Egyptian method of multiplying 5×7 in terms of the distributive property. Answer: $7(5) = 7(1 + 4) = 7 + 28 = 35$

Egyptian Math:
Multiplication and Division

In ancient Egypt, mathematics was a mystery to most people. General math was not taught in schools. People learned only the math they needed for their work. Traders knew how to add and subtract. Surveyors knew how to calculate a right angle. A lot of the math you learn in school—multiplying and dividing fractions, calculating area and volume—was only learned by high officials. Even then, they only learned what they needed to know for calculating the rise and fall of the Nile, collecting taxes, and directing land ownership.

This was partly because the Egyptian system of writing numbers used a different symbol for each multiple of 10. Like Roman numerals, these numbers were fairly easy to add and subtract, but awkward to multiply and divide.

To get around this awkwardness, the Egyptians developed a way to multiply and divide by using addition. To show how this works, we'll multiply 5 by 7.

The first step was to set up two columns of numbers. The first column always started with 1. The second column started with one of the numbers to be multiplied—usually the larger number:

5×7

Column 1	Column 2
1	7

In the next step, you double the number in each column, and write the result on the next row in that column:

5×7

Column 1	Column 2
1	7
2	14

Continue doubling the numbers in each column, and writing the result in the next row, until the number in the first column is greater than the multiplier:

5×7

Column 1	Column 2
1	7
2	14
4	28
8	56

Since 8 is greater than 5, we can stop doubling at this point.

(continued)

Egyptian Math: Multiplication and Division *(continued)*

The next step is to identify the numbers in the first column that add up to the multiplier:

$$5 \times 7$$

Column 1	Column 2
✓ 1	7
2	14
✓ 4	28
8	56
1 + 4 = 5	

Finally, add the numbers in the second column that are in the same row as the marked numbers in the first column:

$$5 \times 7$$

Column 1	Column 2
✓ 1	7 ✓
2	14
✓ 4	28 ✓
8	56
7 + 28 = 35	

Therefore, 5 x 7 = 35

The ancient Egyptians used a similar process for division. To divide 49 by 7, you would again set up two columns. The first column would begin with 1, and the second column would begin with the divisor. Again, double the number in each column and put the sum in the next row, continuing until the number in the second column is greater than the dividend—in this case, 49:

$$49 \div 7$$

Column 1	Column 2
1	7
2	14
4	28
8	56

(continued)

Egyptian Math: Multiplication and Division *(continued)*

Then, by trial and error, find the numbers in the second column that add up to the dividend.

$$49 \div 7$$

Column 1	Column 2
1	7 ✓
2	14 ✓
4	28 ✓
8	56

$7 + 14 + 28 = 49$

The last step is to add the numbers in the first column that are in the same row as the marked numbers in the second column; their sum is equal to the product. If there was no exact answer, the Egyptians chose the closest answers and expressed the rest as a fraction:

$$49 \div 7$$

Column 1	Column 2
✓ 1	7 ✓
✓ 2	14 ✓
✓ 4	28 ✓
8	56

$1 + 2 + 4 = 7$

Therefore, 49 divided by 7 = 7.

On a separate sheet of paper, prepare four simple multiplication problems and four simple division problems. Make sure your division problems have an exact answer. Trade problems with your partner, and use the Egyptian systems of multiplication and division to solve them.

Medicine and Magic: Amulets

OBJECTIVES

Social Studies

- Students will understand some of the scientific developments of ancient Egypt.

Science

- Students will understand the history of science and medicine in Egypt.

Art

- Students will create a three-dimensional object to symbolize a positive attribute of life or society.

MATERIALS

Medicine and Magic: Amulets handout
paper
pencils, markers, paints, paintbrushes
modeling material (air-drying clay, papier-mâché, etc.)
cord to string amulet

BACKGROUND

The history of medicine in Egypt probably goes back to about 4000 B.C.E. Over the many centuries of its development, the field of medicine became a curious mixture of clinical and magical practice.

The Egyptians understood a great deal about human anatomy and had some knowledge of disease. Some of the Middle Kingdom papyri found in Egypt could be called the first medical texts written. One, The Book of Surgery, gives the examining physician clear descriptions of various medical conditions and describes what the doctor should say and do in each situation. For example, one case study involved a man with a wound above the eye:

Examination

If you examine a man having a wound in the top of the eyebrow, penetrating to the bone, you should palpate the wound and draw together for him his gash with stitching.

Diagnosis

You should say concerning him: "One having a wound in his eyebrow. An ailment which I will treat."

Treatment

Now after you have stitched it, you should bind fresh meat upon it the first day. If you find that the stitching of his wound is loose, you should draw it together for him with two strips of plaster, and you should treat it with grease and honey every day until he recovers.

At the same time, there was much Egyptian doctors did not know. They apparently thought that the brain was less important than the other organs and believed that the heart controlled movement. Like doctors all over the world until the nineteenth century, they knew nothing of germs and bacteria and were helpless in the face of infectious disease.

This being so, it is no wonder that medicine and magic should have gone hand in hand. If anything, the wonder should be that ancient Egyptian medicine developed as far as it did. The charms and incantations that formed part of Egypt's approach to medicine were an attempt to fill the gaps in their knowledge.

You might want to remind students that even today we are not fully removed from the days when certain things were considered charms or omens of good or bad luck. How many times have you seen someone hesitate and step aside before walking under a ladder? The person may rationalize about falling buckets, but you know that the decision is really based on superstition, not logic.

PROCEDURE

1. Distribute the handout and discuss it with students. You may wish to limit amulet designs to the Egyptian symbols if you feel that inappropriate symbols may be used.

2. Have students proceed as directed on the handout.

ASSESSMENT

Did students model an amulet (based on an Egyptian design or one of their own) that showed a symbol of strength or protection?

Medicine and Magic: Amulets

Egyptian doctors were the best in the ancient world. Kings and emperors in Persia and other countries relied on them. The Greeks even praised Egyptian doctors in their poetry.

There were good reasons for this fame. Egyptian knowledge of medicine really was advanced for its time. One reason for this was the Egyptian belief in an afterlife beyond death. To enjoy the afterlife, the dead person's body needed to be kept safe. To keep the body safe, the Egyptians developed the process of **embalming**. Through embalming, they learned a lot about the human body.

Egyptian doctors didn't just learn from examining dead bodies. They also carefully observed the living. They noted the symptoms of diseases and experimented with drugs and treatments. When treatments worked—or seemed to work—they were written down on scrolls. New doctors could refer to these scrolls and learn from other doctors' experiences.

Some of the treatments Egyptian doctors used were very successful. They treated broken bones by splinting them with long wooden sticks padded with linen. They knew how to stitch wounds and how to draw the edges of a cut together to prevent scarring. They used drugs like opium as sedatives and made preparations from plants like castor berries, anise, and cassia. These plants are still used for medicinal purposes today. Egyptian doctors even performed surgery, including sawing through the skull to treat head wounds.

Some of their approaches were less successful. One treatment for blindness called for a paste made of pigs' eyes, honey, and red lead. It was injected into the patient's ear. Migraine headaches might be treated by rubbing the head with a fried fish head.

In many cases, doctors were able to recognize and describe the symptoms of a disease, but they had no idea what caused it or how it should be treated. In cases like this, the disease was often attributed to evil forces. When practical medicine failed, some practitioners turned to magic.

In fact, some physicians were also magicians. Lay physicians divided diseases into treatable and untreatable ones; these practitioners knew their own limits. Magician-physicians had no limits. They used magical spells and chants to cure their patients. The following spell was supposed to cure the common cold:

Flow out, poison nose, flow out, son of poison nose! You who breaks bones, destroys the skull, digs in the bone marrow, and makes the seven holes in the head ill!

Since magic was often called on to cure illness, it was natural to use it to try to prevent illness, too. People thought that certain signs and symbols were lucky, or would protect them from harm. These symbols were often worn as lucky charms, or **amulets**, to protect the wearer. Similar amulets were tucked into the wrappings of mummies, to keep the body safe in the afterlife.

(continued)

Medicine and Magic: Amulets *(continued)*

Some charms were thought to give general protection, while some protected the wearer against specific dangers. Here are some common forms for amulets:

 wedjat eye: used to protect against injury

 djed pillar: sign of stability and peace

 sa: general protection against unfriendly forces

 fish: protection against drowning

 ankh: the sign of life, a powerful protective charm

 **scarab beetle:** promising new life, regeneration

 Think about these symbols. Is there any symbol in your life that stands for similar ideas of strength and protection?

Design an amulet to be worn on a cord. The design can be based on one of these Egyptian designs, or it can be a symbol of your own. Remember to include in your design a hole for stringing the amulet. Model your design in clay.

Pierce a hole in the charm and let it dry. Then use paint to decorate it. String a length of cord through your amulet, and wear it in good health.

Justice System: The Eloquent Peasant

OBJECTIVES

Social Studies

- Students will understand that literature can transmit information about a culture.
- Students will see that the concept of justice was an important one to the Egyptians.

Language Arts

- Students will see that literature is developed within a certain context.
- Students will examine a piece of literature from ancient Egypt.
- Students will predict the ending of an incomplete story and develop their own conclusions.

MATERIALS

Justice System: The Eloquent Peasant handout
paper, pens, and pencils

BACKGROUND

Like much literature, the tale of the Eloquent Peasant is more than just a story. It also provides a lot of information about Egyptian society and the Egyptian concept of justice.

The pharaoh was the head of all government. The pharaoh owned all of the land, people, and resources of ancient Egypt. The power this gave the pharaoh was tempered by two things: the need to act according to precedent (essential in a country as bound by tradition as Egypt) and the need to obey the dictates of Ma'at, the goddess of truth, justice, and order. The pharaoh was expected to be the champion of Ma'at on earth and the enemy of all chaos. In theory it was possible for anyone, even the poorest peasant, to approach the pharaoh and make a complaint.

In this story, the peasant's outrage at the injustice done to him suggests that fair and just treatment was the norm, even for peasants. The peasant's direct approach to the minister indicates that he expected to be able to approach this high official easily. It also suggests that he expected to be treated fairly by the minister, despite the fact that his complaint was against the minister's own steward. This is borne out later by the peasant's anger at the way he has been treated, as he accuses the minister of failing to fulfill his sacred duty of ma'at, maintaining the balance by righting injustices.

The Egyptian respect for writing and keeping records can be seen in the fact that the minister has his scribes record everything the peasant says. The peasant is mollified when the minister has the written records read to him; they are proof that the minister has listened and taken him seriously.

Finally, the fact that the pharaoh has been aware all along of the peasant's complaint indicates the level of interest the god-king was supposed to take in all his subjects. Although it is the peasant's unexpected eloquence that piques the interest of both minister and pharaoh, they act in his case because it is right to do so.

In the actual story, justice is served and ma'at is restored. The dishonest steward is beaten and the peasant's donkeys are returned to him.

PROCEDURE

1. Distribute the handout and discuss it with students.

2. If you wish, divide the class into groups.

3. Have students proceed as directed on the handout.

4. Once students have finished their endings for the story, generate a class discussion about the idea of justice. See how many groups finished by returning the peasant's donkeys, and how many left them with the steward. Which ending do students think is most fair? Which do they think is most realistic? Based on clues in the story, which result did the peasant expect? You can model the process of finding information in the text by pointing out one or two clues in the story. For example, point out to students that the peasant was confident he would get justice from the minister and that the minister was immediately willing to hear him. Ask what this suggests to them about Egyptian society. Students should notice the implication that justice was available to everyone, rich and poor.

5. Explain to students that much of our knowledge of history comes from reading the literature of a culture, including fictional stories like this one. The written histories of a people are always biased, but it can be hard to see where the bias lies. While we can't draw any firm conclusions from a story— after all, it is fiction, and only one document—we can develop theories that could be supported or refuted by further study of other documents. Students should see that many historians work this way, developing theories and seeing whether they are borne out by other evidence.

BONUS QUESTION

The peasant compares the minister to the Nile. He should give life and restore balance, as the river does in good years—not overwhelm everything, as the river does in bad years.

ASSESSMENT

Did students write individual paragraphs that addressed all the issues in the prompt: the pharaoh's decision, the peasant's fate, the effect on the steward? Based on the discussion, did students become aware of the importance of the concept of justice in ancient Egyptian society and see how our knowledge of a culture can be increased by reading its literature?

Justice System: The Eloquent Peasant

The history of Egypt is usually divided into three kingdoms and three inter-mediate periods. The Middle Kingdom lasted from about 2040 to 1640 B.C.E.

The **pharaohs** of this period were able to reunite Egypt. They made the borders of the land safe. A number of stories have survived from this time. One of these is the story of "The Eloquent Peasant." For people of ancient Egypt, much of the pleasure of this book came from the eloquent speeches the peasant made. However, tastes in literature vary. Western readers today find the speeches too repetitive. This simplified version of the story leaves out the fine speeches and concentrates on the plot.

Once it happened that a man from the salt field, who had a large family, saw that they had only a little grain left to eat. He loaded his donkeys with salt and set off to trade the salt for food. On the way to town, the road passed between a canal and the wheat fields of one of the pharoah's ministers.

The minister's steward, Thutnakht, saw the man from the salt field approaching. He saw the donkeys loaded with salt and tried to think of a way to take them from the peasant.

Thutnakht hurried to the road with an armful of fine linen cloth. He care-fully spread the linen over the roadway. Then he hid to see what the man from the salt field would do.

The peasant, approaching with his donkeys, stopped when he saw the fine linen. He did not want to drive his donkeys over the white cloth. Their hooves would dirty the linen, even tear it. But he was afraid to bring the donkeys through the wheat fields. They might damage the wheat. And the canal lay on the other side of the road. He could not take his donkeys through the canal.

Finally, he chose the route he thought would do the least harm. He decided to lead the donkeys one by one through the wheat. As he led the fifth donkey through the wheat field, the donkey reached out and pulled a mouthful of wheat.

Thutnakht jumped from his hiding place. "Your donkey has eaten the minis-ter's wheat," he said. "To pay for the damage, I will take your donkeys."

The man from the salt field apologized, and defended his donkeys. But the steward simply had them led away. Then the peasant became angry and accused the steward: "You blocked the public road with your linen. I was only trying to keep from damaging your cloth. It was your fault I had to take my donkeys through the field."

Thutnakht did not reply. He took a branch and beat the man from the salt field until the poor peasant lay gasping on the ground.

(continued)

Justice System: The Eloquent Peasant *(continued)*

Despite the beating, the man from the salt field did not give up. He spent several days trying to talk to Thutnakht and get his donkeys back. When this did not work, he set out to speak to the minister.

When the peasant found the minister, he told the minister what had happened and complained of the injustice. "For ma'at, the sacred principle of truth and justice, has been ignored. It is up to you to right the balance." The minister was impressed by the way the peasant spoke and promised to help him.

When the minister came to the pharaoh, he described his meeting with the man from the salt field. The pharaoh told the minister to listen to the peasant and write down everything he said.

When he appeared once more before the minister, the man from the salt field again demanded that justice should be done. The balance of ma'at must be restored. He said, "Are you not like the Nile who revives the parched fields? Would you become a destroying torrent of water for the man who seeks justice?"

Every day for nine days the minister listened to the peasant's speeches, but did not give him an answer. Finally the man from the salt field worried that his family would run out of food again. He became angry and criticized the minister.

At this the minister yielded. He assured the peasant that he had listened to his arguments. He showed him the scribes, and the records they had made of his words. Finally, the minister went to the pharaoh with the peasant's request for justice.

  How do you think this story should end? Did the pharaoh reject the peasant's suit and send him away empty-handed? Or did he restore ma'at—justice—by punishing the steward and returning the donkeys? Decide what happened next. Then write a paragraph to finish the story.

Bonus Question

In one of his speeches, the peasant uses imagery based on the geography of Egypt. What is the image? Why is it peculiarly Egyptian?

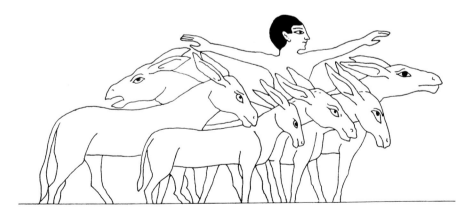

Religion of Egypt:
Hundreds of Gods

OBJECTIVES

Social Studies

- Students will learn about some features of the religion of ancient Egypt.
- Students will become familiar with the major gods of ancient Egypt.
- Students will see how a culture's belief system influences other aspects of the culture.

Art

- Students will prepare a poster showing one or more gods of ancient Egypt.

MATERIALS

Religion of Egypt: Hundreds of Gods handout
Major Deities of Egypt reproducible
paper, markers, paints, other art supplies
optional: reproductions of paintings showing some of the gods of ancient
    Egypt

BACKGROUND

There is something fascinating about the Egyptian pantheon, with its hundreds of gods. The matter-of-fact way the gods are given part-animal, part-human features, and their strong personalities, make an impression on most readers. The stories of the gods, too, are fascinating. Like the gods of Greece and Rome, the gods of Egypt have human emotions and passions, but on a larger scale. The Seth/Osiris/Horus story, with all its subplots, has a lot in common with today's soap operas: deceit, betrayal, villainy, love, seduction, revenge. (See the activity Drama: The Festival of Osiris on page 43 for a summary of this story.)

Although we are most familiar today with the major gods of the state religion, these deities played less part in the daily lives of most Egyptians than the minor local and household gods. In a way, a parallel could be drawn between the Egyptians' attitudes to the local and state gods and Westerners' attitude to news. We watch the national news so that we are informed of current events, but the local news applies to us more personally. In the same way, people in ancient Egypt felt that Ra and Osiris were important, but they were more likely to pray to a household god like Bes.

PREPARATION

Copy the Major Deities of Egypt handout, and cut apart on the lines.

PROCEDURE

1. Decide how you want students to approach this project. Twenty-one gods are listed on pages 38–39. If students work individually, one god can be assigned to each student (some gods may need to be duplicated). Each student should prepare an illustration of the god, labeling the illustration with the name of the god. If students work in groups, you can assign two or three gods to each group. In this case, you have the options of directing students to prepare a separate poster of each god, a composite poster showing several gods, or a frieze-like poster where several gods are shown side by side on a long strip of paper.

2. Distribute the Religion of Egypt handout and discuss it with students.

3. Give students directions for preparing the poster, either as individuals or in groups.

4. Distribute the descriptions of the gods. You may want students to do further research on the god or gods they are to illustrate. Have students prepare posters according to the descriptions.

ASSESSMENT

Did students prepare posters showing the gods as described and directed?

Religion of Egypt: Hundreds of Gods

It's hard to understand Egyptian culture without some understanding of its religion. Religion was part of everything in ancient Egypt.

The many gods of Egypt played a central part in daily life. They were used to explain natural phenomena, like the rising and setting of the sun and moon, the seasons of the year, and the flooding of the Nile. All the forces of nature were represented by the gods.

Some gods had control over a person's whole life and death. These were the important gods of the state religion. Some gods were local. They were important in one village but unheard of in others. Some gods were family or household gods. They were the ones people turned to for help with everyday problems. Although there were hundreds of gods all over Egypt, only a few were worshipped in the same place at the same time.

The Egyptian civilization lasted thousands of years. During that time, many new gods arose. Sometimes a god started off as a local god in one village. If the village became important later, the god became more important, too. Sometimes these gods ended up among the major gods of Egypt.

With so many gods, and new gods being added all the time, the descriptions of some gods ended up overlapping. Sometimes the same god came to be described in different ways, but with the same name. The different descriptions might even contradict each other. This didn't seem to bother the Egyptians. That may be because Egyptian religion wasn't based on faith as much as on ritual. It was more important to learn the right prayers to say than to believe in every part of the descriptions of all the gods.

The gods of the Egyptians were very much like the Egyptians themselves. Although they were often shown with animal heads, their natures were very human. They ate, drank, and wore clothes like humans. Gods and goddesses fell in love and had children. They had feelings and emotions just like humans. Some of the myths, or stories told about the gods, are based on feelings like envy, jealousy, and maternal love.

It would be impossible to describe all the gods of the Egyptians. Still, some were generally more important than others. Most of them were usually shown in one or two ways, so they could be recognized easily. The symbols they wore and carried often came from the hieroglyphics used for their names—a sort of visual pun.

Follow your teacher's directions to make a poster showing some of the major gods of ancient Egypt. Include the name of each god or goddess, either as a label or as part of the poster.

The ancient Egyptians used the gods to explain the mysteries of nature. When there was an earthquake, they came up with a reason for it: Geb, the god of the earth, was laughing.

Major Deities of Egypt

Here are some of the major gods and goddesses of Egypt. The descriptions show what each god meant to the Egyptians, what other gods he or she was related to, and how that god was usually shown.

Amon King of the gods, patron god of the pharaohs. Shown as a bearded man with blue skin and a ram's curved horns, or as a man with a ram's head.	**Bast** Originally symbolizing the warmth of the sun, she later became the goddess of music and dance. She was shown as a cat or a cat-headed woman.	**Hapi** The god of the Nile and bringer of fertility, he was shown as a plump bearded man, colored green or blue. He wore a crown of lilies or papyrus plants on his head.
Anubis God of the dead and of mummification. The son of either Ra or Osiris. Usually shown as a black jackal, or a man with the head of a jackal or a dog.	**Bes** First the protector of the royal house, then the god of recreation, associated with childbirth and protection from dangerous animals. Shown as a dwarf with a large head and goggle eyes, protruding tongue, bowlegs, and a bushy tail.	**Hathor**  The goddess of love, she protected women. She was the daughter of Nut and Ra. Hathor was shown as a woman with the horns of a cow, or with a cow's head.
Atum The creator of the gods, of humans, and of divine order. Shown as an old bearded man wearing the double crown of Upper and Lower Egypt and carrying an ankh, the symbol of life.	**Geb** God of the earth, he held up the world. Son of Shu and Tefnut, husband and brother of Nut. Sometimes shown lying down, with his body as the land and his bent knees the mountains.	**Horus** The god of light, he was represented on earth by the ruling king. The son of Isis and Osiris, opponent of Seth. Shown either as a falcon or as a falcon-headed man.

(continued)

Major Deities of Egypt *(continued)*

Isis
Queen of the gods, the great mother figure. Wife of Osiris, daughter of Nut and Geb, mother of Horus. Shown as a woman wearing a vulture feather headdress topped by either a throne or a disk flanked by horns.

Nekhbet
Goddess of Upper Egypt, the daughter of Ra, protected women in childbirth. Shown as a woman or a vulture wearing the white crown of Upper Egypt, often spreading her wings above the king.

Ra
King of the gods and the chief state god, he personified the sun at its highest point. Shown as a falcon-headed man crowned with the sun disk, carrying an ankh and a scepter.

Khnum
The creator-god, he made people on his potter's wheel. He was shown as a man with the head of a ram and a ram's curving horns.

Nut
Goddess of the sky, daughter of Shu and Tefnut, wife of Geb, mother of Osiris, Isis, Nephthys, and Seth. Shown as a woman arched over the earth, spangled with stars.

Seth
God of storm, chaos, and the desert. Osiris' brother, son of Geb and Nut. Shown as an animal with a greyhound's body, slanting eyes, square-tipped ears, and a long, forked tail.

Ma'at
Goddess of law, truth, and justice, she served as the balance in the scale used to weigh the heart of the deceased. Wife of Thoth. Shown as a woman with an ostrich feather on her head.

Osiris
Originally a fertility god, the giver of agriculture and civilization, later the ruler of the dead. Shown as a dead king in mummy bands holding a crook and flail, wearing the *atef* crown.

Shu
The god of light and air, he supported the sky. Son of Ra, father of Geb and Nut. Shown as a man with an ostrich feather on his head.

Min
God of fertility and the harvest, protector of travelers, god of the road. Son of Ra or Shu. Shown as a bearded man wearing a crown with two tall plumes on top and a flail or thunderbolt in his right hand.

Ptah
God of fertility, creator of the universe, patron of crafts and art. Shown as a mummified man with a shaved head, holding a *djed* symbol and scepter.

Thoth
God of the moon, science, and knowledge, scribe of the gods, lord of magic. Husband of Ma'at. Shown as a man with the head of an ibis, topped with a crescent moon and disk.

Drama: The Festival of Osiris

OBJECTIVES

Social Studies

- Students will understand how belief systems like religion can affect other parts of a culture.
- Students will become familiar with one of the central myths of ancient Egypt.

Language Arts

- Students will write a script based on a myth.

Art

- Students will create animal-head masks.

MATERIALS

The Festival of Osiris handout
paper and pens
optional: materials for making masks, props

BACKGROUND

Osiris was seen in ancient Egypt as the god of rebirth and resurrection. He was the first king to survive death and the first to be mummified. As the Egyptian rites of mummification developed, the god Anubis, who said the spells that preserved Osiris, was held to oversee the process of embalming.

Pharaohs were considered the successors of Osiris and Horus. In life the pharaohs were likened to Horus, who ruled the kingdom of the living. In death they became one with Osiris, who ruled in the kingdom of the dead.

The eye that Horus lost in his fight with Seth became a symbol of victory over evil. Known as the *wedjat* eye, it was used as a protective amulet. (See the activity on amulets and medicine on page 27.)

PROCEDURE

1. Distribute the handout and discuss it with students.

2. Demonstrate breaking the story down into short phrases. As a class, break the entire story down. You may record the phrases the class generates, or appoint a student to act as recorder.

3. Go through the completed list to make sure nothing essential has been omitted and nothing nonessential has been included.

4. Divide the list of phrases into acts and scenes, based on how they connect to each other. One possible division might look like this:

Act I

Scene 1:   Brothers marry
Brothers receive dominions

Scene 2:   Osiris rules well
Seth is jealous

Scene 3:   Seth brings chest to banquet
Osiris steps into chest
Seth closes lid, throws chest in river
Osiris drowns

Act II

Scene 1:   Isis searches for and finds body
Isis miraculously pregnant by dead Osiris
Isis hides body in delta

Scene 2:   Seth finds body
Seth dismembers body, scatters remains
Isis finds pieces
Isis binds body with linen
Isis, Anubis say spells to preserve body

Scene 3:   Horus is born
Horus grows up hidden in delta

Act III

Scene 1:   Adult Horus seeks out Seth
Seth, Horus fight
Horus loses eye
Seth beaten

Scene 2:   Seth, Horus go before gods
Horus named Osiris' heir
Seth banished

Scene 3:   Thoth places eye of Horus on Osiris
Osiris sees possibility of new life
Osiris becomes king of the Afterlife

5. Divide class into groups. Allocate scenes to groups so that each group has about the same amount of material.

6. If you wish, direct each group to make one or more masks for the performance. Masks should be made for the main characters—Isis, Osiris, Seth,

Anubis, Thoth. Other characters—Nephthys, Geb, Nut, the tribunal of gods—can be played without masks, although masks would add to the performance. The activity on pages 38–39, Major Deities of Egypt, describes the appearance of the major gods, and illustrations can be found in many books.

7. When all groups have prepared their scenes, combine the scripts to form a whole play. Choose students to read the script for each part, then present the play. It can be given as a dramatic reading, in which students remain in their seats, or staged as a play.

ASSESSMENT

Did students successfully convert a narrative into a dramatic script and present the script as a reading or performance?

VARIATION

Under the pharaohs, the roles in the Osiris drama were played by live actors. Later, under Ptolemaic rule, the play was sometimes performed as a puppet show. Have students create puppets for the main characters of the play and present it as a puppet show.

EXTENSION ACTIVITY

The Osiris myth is central to Egyptian culture. The concept of mummification and life after death is based on Osiris' reanimation by Isis and Anubis. The ruling pharaoh was identified with Horus as the living embodiment of the god, and with Osiris after death. Direct students to investigate the different ways in which this myth affected Egyptian religion and society.

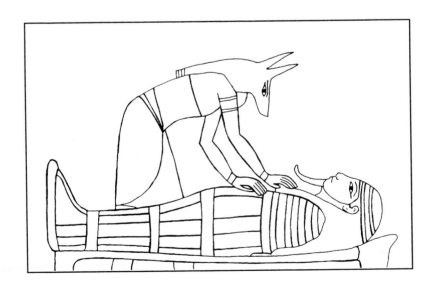

Drama: The Festival of Osiris

Egyptian literature is full of stories, poems, and proverbs. But plays don't seem to have been common. In fact, the only plays we know about are of a type called passion plays or mystery plays. Mystery plays usually have a religious theme. They act out a scene or a story to do with religion.

One well-known mystery play was performed every year in Abydos. According to legend, the god Osiris was buried at Abydos. The mystery play there told the story of his life and how he became the ruler of the Afterlife. The play was probably performed by priests wearing masks to play the parts of the main characters. They acted out events in the story of Osiris. Here is one version of that story:

Osiris and Seth were both sons of Geb and Nut, the god of the earth and the goddess of the sky. Seth was given the desert and the sky over it to rule. He married his sister Nephthys. Osiris was given the Nile and the fruit-bearing earth. He married his sister Isis.

Osiris was a good ruler. He brought civilization and agriculture to Egypt. His subjects loved him.

Seth, ruler of the empty desert, was jealous of his brother and decided to murder him. Osiris was tall, taller than other men. Seth decided to use this fact in his plan.

He had a chest made that was exactly Osiris' size. It was a beautiful thing, carved and painted. When Seth brought it to a feast at Osiris' house, everyone stared at the chest. Everyone wanted it. When Seth said he would give the chest to the one who fitted in it, all the guests were eager to try. They were all too short for the box. Finally Osiris stepped into the chest and lay down. The box was exactly his size.

Before Osiris could stand up, Seth and his helpers slammed the lid of the chest. They fastened it tightly and threw it into the Nile. Osiris was carried away by the current and drowned.

Isis, Osiris' wife, set out to find her husband's body. After a long search, she found it and brought it back to Egypt. Miraculously, she became pregnant by her dead husband. To keep Osiris' body safe, she hid it in the marshes of the delta, where the Nile flows into the sea.

The evil Seth was still jealous of his dead brother. Seth found where Isis had hidden the body, and waited until she left it unguarded. Then Seth pulled the body from the coffin and tore it into pieces. He threw the pieces in all directions, so that no two pieces lay in the same place.

Isis again set out to find her husband's body. At last she found all the pieces. She used linen strips to bind the limbs together. Then Anubis, the guardian of the dead, helped her to preserve the body with magic spells.

(continued)

Drama: The Festival of Osiris (continued)

When Isis' son was born she named him Horus. She hid the boy so well that his uncle Seth never even knew he had been born. When Horus was grown he went to look for his father's murderer. The battle between Seth and Horus was fierce. Horus lost one eye in the fight, but he overcame Seth.

Even so, Seth wouldn't admit that Horus should be his father's heir and rule over Egypt. The quarrel between them was brought to the gods for judgment.

The gods recognized Horus as his father's successor. Horus became the ruler of Egypt. Seth, now known as the personification of evil, was sent away.

Then Thoth, the god of wisdom, took the eye that Horus had lost. He placed it over the heart of the dead Osiris. Through this, the heart was given the gift of sight. It saw that another life existed beyond life on earth. Osiris rose up again. He became king of the Afterlife, where he ruled as a god.

Can you see how this story could be turned into a play? Start by finding the major points of the story. Ignore anything that doesn't move the plot ahead. What happens in each paragraph? Who does what? How do the other characters react? Prepare a list of short phrases that summarize all of the action. Now divide the phrases into groups that seem to go together. Some parts of the plot work together to build up to something. Group those parts together.

Now, working in your group, prepare a script for one part of the play. Write a dialogue that explains what happens.

As a class, combine all the parts of the play into one complete script. Decide who should read the script for each character. Finally, present the play.

Osiris   Isis   Horus

Playing Games in Ancient Egypt

OBJECTIVES

Both Games:

Social Studies

- Students will learn about pastimes in ancient Egypt.
- Students will see the continuity of human interest in certain areas.

Math

- Students will learn about mathematical games of ancient Egypt.

The Finger Game:

Social Studies

- Students will see how an ancient game is played today.

Math

- Students will explore probability through a game-playing situation.

Nine-Men's Morris:

Math

- Students will use logic to develop a playing strategy.

Art

- Students will make a game board.

MATERIALS

Playing Games in Ancient Egypt handouts
For Nine-Men's Morris:
  paper
  18 buttons, pebbles, or game counters, 9 each in two different colors

BACKGROUND

Tomb drawings like the one redrawn on page 46 show Egyptians playing the finger game. A similar game is still played in many parts of the Mediterranean today.

Variations of Nine-Men's Morris are played in many lands. Designs for similar games have been found cut into Greek and Roman pavements. Games of this type were played by the Vikings, Russians, French, and Germans. Shakespeare refers to an English version in *A Midsummer Night's Dream*, Act II, Scene I. Like many other games of strategy, the simple rules are deceptive; the game itself can be quite complex.

PREPARATION

Students can play one or both games. The handouts are set up so that you can reproduce the general information about games with the instructions for the finger game. The instructions for Nine-Men's Morris are on separate sheets so that you can choose to include them or use only the finger game in your lesson.

PROCEDURE

1. Distribute the handout(s) and discuss with students.

2. Students proceed as directed on the handout(s).

ASSESSMENT

Were students able to play one or both games successfully? Did students develop strategies for play?

VARIATIONS

- A group version of the finger game can also be played. In this version, one player is It. The other players form a ring with their backs to the player who is It, who stands in the center of the ring. The player who is It extends one or more fingers, as in the two-person version of the game. The players in the ring take turns calling out the number they think it is, then turning to face the center of the ring so that they can see the player who is It. These players cannot comment on the actual number of fingers they see. When all players have guessed, the first one who guessed the correct number becomes It.

- A Nine-Men's Morris tournament can be set up by having small groups play among themselves, then the winner from each group plays the winners of other groups. Each game can be an elimination game, or students can play for the best two games out of three.

- Direct students to prepare a Nine-Men's Morris board using tagboard. The board should be decorated with Egyptian symbols to make it as attractive as possible.

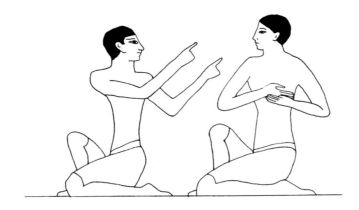

Playing Games in Ancient Egypt: The Finger Game

Paintings and models found in Egypt often show people at work. But many also show people relaxing and enjoying themselves at various games and sports. Children in ancient Egypt had dolls, balls, and rolling toys with heads and legs that moved. They swam, wrestled, and practiced archery. Amusements for adults included music, listening to storytellers, hunting, and fishing.

People also played board games like *senet* and the serpent game. Senet was particularly popular. Game boards and pieces have been found in several tombs. Unfortunately, the rules for both these games have been lost.

However, some of the other games played in ancient Egypt are similar to games played today. They may even be later versions of the same games, still popular after thousands of years.

The Finger Game

No special equipment is needed to play the finger game. To play this game, two players sit facing each other with their hands behind their backs. On the count of three, both players put their right hands in front of them with one or more fingers outstretched. At the same time both players say how many fingers they think will be extended in all (between 2 and 10). A player who guesses the total correctly wins that round of the game.

A similar game, called *mora*, is played in much of the Mediterranean area today. It is often used to make a decision—who pays for a cold drink, who goes to get the pizza.

With a partner, play 10 rounds of the finger game. Did either of you guess the correct number of fingers on all 10 rounds, or on any of the rounds? Decide how many possible answers there are for a given round. Then work out the probability that a player will guess the correct answer. Do the results of your play match the probability?

In another version of the finger game, each player either extends one finger or keeps the hand closed. Decide how changing the play in this way would affect the possible number of answers, and the probability of guessing the right number of fingers. Now play 10 rounds of this version of the game. Were your results in line with probability this time?

Work with your partner to see if there are strategies to playing this game. If you find one, take turns using this strategy to play.

   Hands-on Culture of Ancient Egypt

Playing Games in Ancient Egypt: Nine Men's Morris

Designs for a game like Nine Men's Morris were found cut into the roofing slabs of a temple at Kurna, in Egypt. They date to about 1400 B.C.E. Similar games have been found throughout Europe.

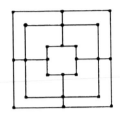

Points on the board

This is a game for two players. Each player uses nine counters. The game is played on the 24 points marked. (A point is a place where two lines meet or where one line forms a corner.) Play starts with no counters on the board. Players take turns placing one counter on a point on the game board. The object of the game is to get three counters in a line.

When all the pieces have been placed on the board, each player can move one counter per turn to the next empty point along a line. No points can be skipped in making moves.

When a player gets three counters in a row, that player can remove one piece belonging to the other player. Counters that are already in a line of three cannot be removed unless there are no other counters of that color on the board. As soon as a new line of three is formed, an opponent's piece can be removed.

Play continues like this until one player has only three counters left. Any of these counters can now hop to any empty point on the board. They need not move to the next empty point along a line. If the second player is also reduced to three pieces, these pieces can also hop. The game ends when one player is reduced to two counters. The player who still has three counters is the winner.

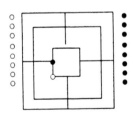

White plays first. Here is the board after one play for both players.

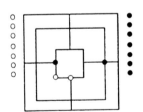

This is the board after two plays for both players.

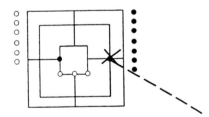

White has played for the third time and has three counters in a row. White removes one black piece from the game.

(continued)

Playing Games in Ancient Egypt:
Nine Men's Morris *(continued)*

Copy the board design below onto a piece of paper. Then try this game for yourself.

This game is related to the simple three-in-a-row game tic-tac-toe. In tic-tac-toe a simple strategy gives the first player the advantage. The first player should always either win or draw the game. Is there a similar strategy for playing Nine Men's Morris?

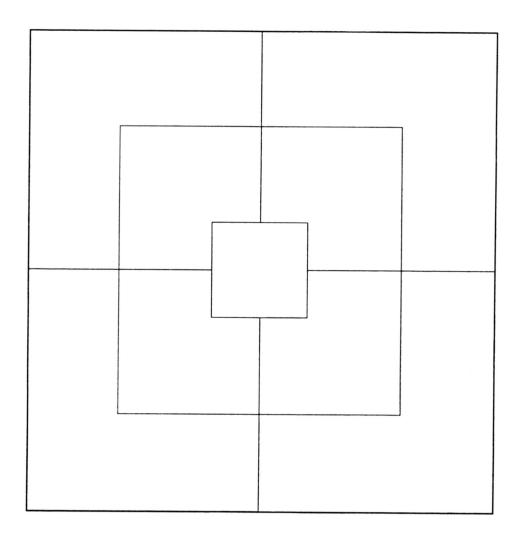

   Hands-on Culture of Ancient Egypt

Packing for the Afterlife

OBJECTIVES

Social Studies

- Students will understand that different cultures have similar basic needs.
- Students will understand why many different articles were buried in Egyptian tombs with the deceased.
- Students will understand how the Egyptian belief system affected other areas of their culture.

Art (optional)

- Students will create two- or three-dimensional representations of objects they would wish to have in an afterlife.

MATERIALS

Packing for the Afterlife handout
pencils, paper
optional: art supplies, modeling materials

BACKGROUND

At the time of the Old Kingdom, the Afterlife in the Field of Reeds could only be enjoyed by the pharaoh. By the time of the Middle Kingdom, the Field of Reeds was open to everyone. To be sure of a comfortable and prosperous eternity, wealthy people stocked their tombs well. An inventory of tomb goods divided into the headings on the student page might look like this:

Food

bread	cake
lentils	ox
beans	wine
cucumbers	beer
onions	milk
lettuce	dates
leeks	figs
garlic	melons
fish	grapes
duck	pomegranates
goose	spices
olive oil	honey

Clothes

pleated linen kilts	linen tunics
papyrus sandals	leather sandals

Entertainment

writing:

papyrus	reed pens and ink palettes

games:

senet boards	serpent game boards
throw sticks for gambling games	

musical instruments:

drums	tambourines
harps	flutes
lutes	sistrums

sports equipment:

bows and arrows	throwing sticks for hunting
fishing tackle	

Furniture

wooden headrests	chairs
beds	tables

Cosmetics

green eye paint (from crushed malachite)
black eye kohl (from galena)
red lip color (from iron oxide)

perfume	perfume bottles
makeup palettes	scented oils and salves

Household goods

drinking cups	glass jars
pottery bowls	oil lamps
model boat	

Personal belongings

razors	hairpins
combs	mirrors of polished metal

jewelry:

amulets	collars	rings
necklaces	pectorals	bracelets
scarabs	earplugs	anklets

As well as all of this, the tomb of a well-off person would include models of different types of servants to do the household tasks (see the Model Workers activity on page 61) and *shabti* figures to work in the fields of Osiris in place of the deceased.

The tombs of the poor were far less lavish. The deceased was usually buried with some food, a few dishes, and whatever personal belongings the household could spare. In the Afterlife, as in this life, there was a gulf between rich and poor.

PROCEDURE

1. Distribute the handout and discuss it with students. You may wish to use the composite list on these pages to model, giving reasons for choices. Or, you may want to offer some choices of your own and explain why you would pick those things. Choose one category and brainstorm items that might be included.

2. Have students proceed as directed on the handout.

3. When all lists have been completed, choose one or two categories. Ask a few students to read their lists. How much do they have in common? Do students think that the tombs of ancient Egyptians would contain roughly the same things?

ASSESSMENT

Read students some of the items listed under the headings on page 51. Which Egyptian categories have most in common with the student-generated lists? Which have least in common? Ask students to suggest reasons for both the overlap and the variance. Can they draw any conclusions about human needs in general from this activity?

VARIATION

Egyptian tombs often contained paintings and models of items needed in the Afterlife, in case the actual item was damaged. Have students paint or model some of the items on their lists.

EXTENSION ACTIVITY

Give students the list of foods common in Egypt on page 50. Explain that these were the kinds of food rich people ate, not the poor people of Egypt. Have students classify these foods according to the four food groups. Did ancient Egyptians eat a balanced diet?

Packing for the Afterlife

In Egypt under the pharaohs, an average 15-year-old could expect to live about 25 more years. An average 15-year-old in America today can expect to live about 60 more years. When you compare those numbers, you may think that Egyptians didn't live very long.

Most Egyptians wouldn't have agreed with you. They believed that there was another life waiting for them after death. They would live forever in the Field of Reeds. This was like a perfect version of the Egypt they already knew. They would eat the same food, wear the same clothes, and play the same games there as they did in this life.

The only catch was that the Egyptians had to bring everything with them. They had to make sure the *ka*, or eternal soul, would have enough food to last forever. Otherwise they might starve to death in the hereafter! They had to provide clothes, food, furniture, games—anything that they wanted to be able to enjoy in the Field of Reeds. That's why Egyptian tombs had so many things in them. Their owners wanted to be able to enjoy eternity without saying "Oh, I wish I'd remembered to bring my favorite pair of sandals."

Sometimes, the tomb owners didn't put the actual item they wanted in the tomb. They put in a model of the thing instead. One reason for this was space. If they had really put everything they wanted in the tomb, there wouldn't be room for the coffin. For example, most transportation in Egypt was by boat. The Nile was the country's main highway. In order to travel in the Afterlife, most people would want to have a boat available, but it would take up a lot of room. So small models of boats, complete with model sailors, were put in the tombs.

If you've ever tried to pack for vacation, or even to spend the night at a friend's house, you know how hard it can be to remember everything you need. You always seem to forget one or two things that you just can't do without. Can you imagine what it would be like to have to pack for eternity?

(continued)

Name _____ Date _____

Packing for the Afterlife *(continued)*

The things often put in Egyptian tombs can be grouped under a few general headings: **food, clothes, entertainment, furniture, cosmetics, household goods,** and **personal belongings**. Food might include models of bread and cakes, fruit and vegetables, meat and poultry. For entertainment, people brought game boards, hunting and fishing gear, writing tools, and musical instruments. Personal belongings might include mirrors made of polished metal, combs and hairpins, and jewelry. Many people also brought along pets for the Afterlife. Cats were the most popular pets in ancient Egypt. A lot of people also had dogs. Some even had monkeys or gazelles as pets.

 Use these general headings to make up your own list of things to pack for eternity. On a separate piece of paper, write each heading: **food, clothes, entertainment, furniture, cosmetics, household goods, personal belongings**. List at least four things under each heading. Beside each item on your list, make a brief note saying why you would bring it. How is your list different from the things that an ancient Egyptian might have wanted to take?

Bread was the most important food for most Egyptians—so important they had 15 different words for it!

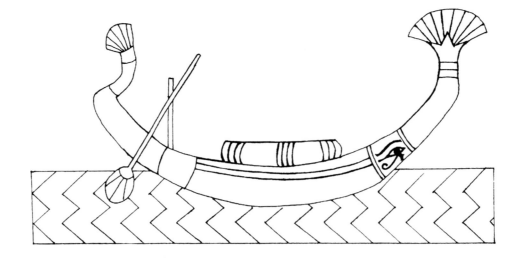

© 1997 J. Weston Walch, Publisher   54   *Hands-on Culture of Ancient Egypt*

Making a Mummy

OBJECTIVES

Social Studies

- Students will see how a belief system can affect other aspects of a culture.

Science

- Students will learn about the history of knowledge of human anatomy.
- Students will learn of some of the diseases suffered by early people.
- Students will understand how the process of mummification works.

Art

- Students will make a model of a mummy.

MATERIALS

Making a Mummy handout
self-hardening clay or other modeling material
adhesive white fabric tape
scissors
paints (including gold, if possible), markers
paintbrushes
optional: salt, eggplant, two colanders or sieves, two plates

BACKGROUND

The word *mummy* comes from the Arabic word *mummiya*, meaning "bitumen." This was because the blackened resin on mummies was mistaken for bitumen.

The first Egyptian mummies were probably an accident of nature. The soil of Egypt was limited to a narrow strip along the Nile, sometimes as little as a few hundred feet wide. Because so little land was available for farming, the Egyptians did not want to set any of it aside as a burial place for the dead. Instead, they buried their dead in the sand, where nothing could be grown. Early graves were simply shallow holes dug in the sand. The body was placed in the grave, then covered with more sand. Rocks were often piled on top, both to mark the grave and to keep animals away.

The Egyptians soon discovered that this actually preserved the body. The hot, dry sand around the body pulled all the moisture out of the skin and other organs. The bacteria didn't have time to get to work. The body was dried out, a natural mummy.

As the civilization along the Nile grew, rich people started to want something more substantial for a grave than a hole dug in the sand. Tombs were built, and the bodies were wrapped in cloth before burial. The wrapped bodies were placed in a tightly closed coffin. Instead of just digging holes in the ground, Egyptians built tombs to provide a secure resting place for the body of the deceased.

The unfortunate effects of this new approach to burial were probably discovered when the tombs were plundered by grave robbers. With the moisture of the body sealed in and the hot, drying sand kept away, the body within its wrappings quickly decayed.

People started looking for a way to preserve bodies *and* have fancy tombs. Mummification was the solution.

Since mummification was practiced in Egypt for thousands of years, the process varied somewhat over time. New traditions were developed and added on to the old, although old traditions were rarely discarded. One change, introduced by the twenty-first dynasty (1085–945 B.C.E.), was the attempt to create more natural-looking mummies. During the drying process, the body of the mummy shrank and the skin became wizened and leathery. Because the *ka* and *ba* had to be able to recognize the body in order to return to it, embalmers began to try to restore some of the original appearance of the body. Slits were made in the skin of the face, arms, necks, and legs, and filling materials were inserted under the skin. Various materials were used as filling, including linen packing, sawdust, ashes, mud, and sand. The aim was to plump up the face and limbs to make them more attractive—like an early version of cosmetic surgery. Artificial eyes of painted linen, stone, or gold might be placed over the mummy's own eyes. Some mummies were given wigs and false eyebrows made of human hair.

Of course, all these elaborate processes were expensive, and therefore reserved for the rich. Cheaper approaches to mummification included injecting the body with cedar oil and using a less expensive oil for the process. Even these methods were out of the reach of most poor people. They were still buried in the way their ancestors had been buried: wrapped simply in linen cloth and placed in a hole in the sand. It is ironic that many of these bodies are better preserved today than the bodies of the wealthy. The natural mummification process, combined with the damage done to wealthy tombs by grave robbers, made these simple graves a better way to provide an eternal home for the *ka*.

PROCEDURE

1. Distribute the handout and discuss it with students.

2. If you wish, divide students into groups.

3. Have students proceed as directed on the handout.

VARIATIONS

- The figures made in this activity resemble the shabti figures, or "answerers," buried in some tombs. To capitalize on this resemblance, you can make the base figure out of wood. Have a shabti figure shape cut from half-inch-thick pine, then smooth the edges with sandpaper. Students should proceed as directed from step 2.

- The base figure can also be shaped from other modeling materials, like papier-mâché, or cut from an easily worked substance like BalsaFoam.

- Instead of fabric tape, use plaster of paris bandages, cut into strips, for the wrapping. The strips should be small enough to handle easily, as the plaster dries quickly. Students should dampen the strips in water and carefully wrap the mummy with them, smoothing the plaster with their fingers. Plaster left on the hands should be wiped off with a paper towel or rag before washing the hands; if the plaster is washed down the sink, it can clog drains.

- Fabric binding (sold in fabric and craft stores) or old sheets cut into strips can also be used as an alternative to adhesive fabric tape. Using nonadhesive strips makes it essential to maintain tension on the strips as you wrap, or the whole thing will come apart. As each strip is completed, coat it with a quick-drying glue to mimic the resin used by the Egyptians.

ASSESSMENT

Did students successfully make and wrap a model mummy?

EXTENSION ACTIVITY

Salt and an eggplant can be used to show how the water can be drawn out of soft tissues. Place two colanders or sieves on two plates. Cut the eggplant into rounds. Arrange a few rounds in the bottom of each colander or sieve. Sprinkle the slices in one colander liberally with salt. After a few minutes, beads of moisture will start to appear on the salted eggplant. After 20 to 30 minutes, liquid will start to pool on the plate below as the salt pulls the liquid out of the vegetable tissues. The unsalted eggplant will remain dry to the touch.

Making a Mummy

For many Egyptians, life after death was an important part of religious faith. They believed that the soul did not die with the body. The soul needed just two things to live forever: food, and an image of the living person to use as a resting place.

To provide food for the soul, Egyptians buried food, and models of food, with the dead person. To provide a resting place, they tried to keep the dead body as intact as possible.

This meant fighting nature. Decay is part of the natural cycle for plants, animals, and people. Anything that lives has to die eventually. Once the organism dies, it starts to break down, or decay. Bacteria—organisms so small they can't be seen without a microscope—start to break down the dead tissues. Soon the original shape changes. It no longer looks the way it did when it was alive.

Bacteria grow best in a moist environment. Since the human body is between 60 and 75 percent water, it is a great place for bacteria to grow. This made it hard for the ancient Egyptians to keep bodies looking like people. The process they developed to make it easier is called **mummification**. The main idea in mummification is getting all of the water out of the body.

As soon as someone who could afford mummification died, the body was given to the priests and embalmers. The family knew that the process took about 70 days, so they started to plan the funeral while the body was embalmed.

The embalming process was overseen by a priest who wore a jackal-head mask. He stood for Anubis, the guardian of the dead.

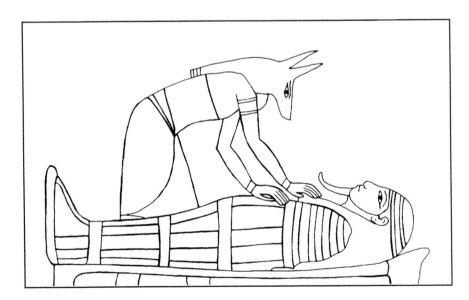

(continued)

Making a Mummy *(continued)*

The first stage in mummification was taking the internal organs out of the body. Otherwise the body would decay from the inside out. To do this, the embalmers cut the stomach open and took out the stomach, lungs, liver, and intestines. They usually left the heart, as it was needed for an important ceremony in the Afterlife. The brain was removed by slipping a hook through one nostril and pulling it out!

After the organs were removed, the body was washed with a sweet-smelling liquid. Then the body was packed, inside and out, with natron. Natron is a natural salt found by lakes in the desert. It acted a bit like the crystals packed with delicate electronic equipment today to keep it dry. The natron pulled the moisture away from the surfaces it touched. The organs taken out of the body were treated in the same way.

The body was left in the natron for about 40 days. It was washed again, then dried, and coated in oils and resins to stop decay. The cut in the stomach where the organs had been removed was pulled together and covered with a seal bearing the Eye of Horus, a powerful charm.

Then the wrapping process began. This could take another 15 days, and use as much as 150 yards of linen. Strips of varied widths and lengths were used for different parts of the body. Some of them had the dead person's name written on the ends. Some were marked with figures of gods or magic formulae to help the dead person journey through the Afterlife.

The bandaging began with the feet and legs, then the hands and arms. The main part of the body came next, and finally the head. Slowly, the body was covered in layers of linen. As many as 20 layers could be used; the wrappings could be as much as two inches thick. As each layer was applied, it was coated in warm resin to keep moisture away from the body. Amulets (good luck charms) were placed among the wrappings. They were supposed to keep the body safe.

Finally, a mask representing the dead person's face was put on the mummy. The face usually didn't look much like the person. It was idealized to make the person look better. Putting a portrait on the mummy was supposed to help the soul find its way back to the body.

To prepare for burial, the completed mummy was put in a mummy case. Sometimes this was put inside another coffin, like nesting dolls. Both the mummy case and the coffin were usually covered with images of gods and magic symbols. These were to help the dead person's soul in the kingdom of the dead.

The ancient Egyptians probably learned a lot about human anatomy from the mummification process. Scientists today have learned a lot from mummies, too. We know that people in ancient Egypt suffered from a lot of the same diseases we do. Since they had no immunization against diseases like smallpox and polio, more people had these illnesses. We know how the food they ate affected their health, and how their doctors treated their illnesses.

(continued)

Making a Mummy *(continued)*

In this activity, you will make your own version of a mummy—leaving out the parts about removing the organs and drying the body with salt!

1. Begin by using the clay to make a figure roughly the shape of a human. Since you will be wrapping the figure in "bandages," you don't need details for the body. The head and headdress, arms, and shoulders should be clearly modeled. This will be the base for your mummy. Let the figure dry.

2. Cut three or four lengths of adhesive cloth tape. Begin with pieces about six inches long until you get used to the process. Use the tape to wrap your mummy, starting at the feet.

3. When your mummy is completely wrapped, you are ready to paint the portrait mask. You may find it easiest to apply the background color first (the Egyptians often used gold) and then add the details with black paint. Your mummy is complete!

> Egypt has the oldest tourism industry in the world. As long as 2,000 years ago, Greeks and Romans traveled to Egypt to see the country's ancient monuments. They even left graffiti behind!

Model Workers

OBJECTIVES

Social Studies

- Students will see the purpose of model figures found in tombs.

- Students will express an aspect of their lives in the context of another culture.

Art

- Students will create a three-dimensional figure performing an activity or task.

MATERIALS

Model Workers handout
modeling materials (self-drying clay; regular clay if you have access to a kiln)
paints
paintbrushes

BACKGROUND

Another kind of model worker was also included in many tombs. These were called *shabti* figures, or "answerers." They were usually shown as miniature mummies, inscribed with Chapter Six of the Book of the Dead. Their purpose was to work in the fields of Osiris in the place of the dead person. The lifelike figures referred to in this activity were to work *for* the dead person, not instead of him or her.

PROCEDURE

1. Distribute the Model Workers handout and discuss it with students.

2. If you wish, have students brainstorm to come up with jobs they hate to do, like homework, washing dishes, cleaning their bedrooms, baby-sitting, mowing the lawn.

3. Have students proceed as directed on the handout.

4. When all models are completed, display them in the classroom.

ASSESSMENT

Did students make a model of a person doing a job they would like to be excused from doing?

Model Workers

A lot of what we know about life in ancient Egypt comes from the tombs of rich people. The Egyptians believed that everyone consisted of two parts: the body, which would eventually die, and the spirit, or *ka*, which could live forever. They believed that when the body died, the *ka* went to the kingdom of the god Osiris. This kingdom was like a mirror image of Egypt, with a river and fertile fields, but everything there was perfect. The *ka* of the dead person could live forever in the kingdom of the dead.

The Egyptian afterlife sounds a lot like the Western idea of heaven, but there was one big difference. In the Egyptian afterlife, there was still work to be done. The fields had to be plowed, cloth had to be woven, food had to be prepared. If you were wealthy when you were alive, you had servants to do all the hard work. But who would do the work for you in the afterlife?

To make sure they didn't have to spend eternity doing the work they'd managed to avoid in life, rich Egyptians placed little models of workers in their tombs. When the *ka* came back to life, these workers would also come to life and take care of all the hard work. Models of all kinds of workers have been found in tombs. There are farmers to plow and sow the crop, reapers to cut the grain, millers to grind it, and bakers to turn it into bread. There are porters to carry heavy loads. There are spinners and weavers, scribes and musicians, potters and carpenters—workers to do all the jobs the wealthy Egyptians didn't want to do themselves.

Each model is like a small scene. It may show a single figure, like a porter carrying a load of goods on his head. It may show two or three figures together, like a group of women spinning flax and weaving linen from the thread. Some models even show large groups, like a model of a granary with workers carrying grain, grinding it, and loading the flour, while scribes keep track of the work.

 Is there some job you have to do that you'd like to avoid for all eternity? Think of all the things you have to do on a regular basis, and choose the one thing you would most like to stop doing. Now design a model worker to do the job for you. Your model should be about six inches tall, and should show someone doing the job you want to get out of.

Let your model dry, then add details with paint.

> The first strike recorded in history took place in Thebes, an ancient city in southern Egypt on the Nile River. Workers who had waited months for their wages refused to work any more. They left the workers' quarters and chanted "We are hungry" until they received what they were owed.

The Game of the Afterlife

OBJECTIVES

Social Studies

• Students will understand what Egyptians believed would happen to them after death.

• Students will see how religious belief can affect other aspects of a culture.

Art

• Students will create a game board.

• Students will create a visual interpretation of a narrative.

MATERIALS

The Game of the Afterlife handout
poster board
pencils, paints, markers, other art supplies
dice
buttons or other small objects to use as playing pieces
optional: books of Egyptian designs, samples of other board games like
    Monopoly, Snakes and Ladders, etc.

BACKGROUND

During the time of the Old Kingdom, only the pharaoh and his immediate circle had the opportunity to achieve eternal life in the Field of Reeds. Later, this became an option for everybody. Of course, there were always people who didn't believe in Osiris and the Afterlife, but for many, life after death was a reality. These people did what they could to prepare for the ordeal of crossing the underworld, and for having supplies to last the soul for eternity.

To meet the physical needs of the soul after death, people arranged to have their bodies preserved as well as they could, and had models and paintings of things they would need placed in their tombs. And to try to safeguard the soul in its journey through Duat—the place of departed spirits—those who could afford them bought copies of the Book of the Dead. These books contained spells to help the *ba* with the various perils of the underworld. Spells included the names of the 12 gates and their guardians, the names of the 42 judges and the sin each punished, and spells to pass safely through the 12 hells. Amulets, or good luck charms, were placed among the wrappings of the mummy, both to safeguard the body itself and to help the *ba* on its journey.

Because of the linear nature of this journey, it is ideally suited to the development of a board game. Each player starts at the edge of the Lake of Dawn, and hopes to finish before the throne of Osiris.

The Snakes and Ladders approach is the simplest to set up. The board is divided into squares, and some of the dangers and successes of the journey are written in some of the squares. Snakes are an appropriate symbol for the dangers that move a player backwards, as the *ba* must face snakes and serpents at several points in its journey. Instead of ladders, students might use a stream of water, symbolizing the Winding Water along which the *ba* travels, or a papyrus boat, symbolizing the boat in which the *ba* sails. Some squares might contain pitfalls like "forgot the name of the third gate," which would send the player back to an earlier point in the game. Some might list positive events, like "passed the terrible serpent Apophis," which would move the player along more quickly. The dangers and successes should be in order on the board—first the lake and ferryman, then the 12 realms, then the Hall of the Two Truths.

Other board games can be based simply on the roll of dice, or can include spaces where the player must either go to a certain point or draw a card from a pile. The cards can be structured like the spaces on the Snakes and Ladders game. Some can be pitfalls that carry penalties. Some can be lucky chances that carry rewards. Some can even be good-luck amulets (like those described in the activity on page 30, Medicine and Magic), which the player can use to fend off some future peril.

PROCEDURE

1. Form groups.

2. Distribute the handout and discuss it with students. If you wish, you can show examples of commercial board games and brainstorm ways in which their formats could be adapted for the journey through the Afterlife. You may choose to direct all groups to use one game format, or you may let them choose the format. In either case, stress the importance of developing clear rules, and writing them out so that others can easily play the game.

3. Have students proceed as directed on the handout.

ASSESSMENT

When all games have been completed, set up a system for having students try out one another's games. A game is successful if it includes at least 10 stages of the journey through Duat in the correct order, it is attractively laid out, and other students are able to grasp the rules and play the game.

The Game of the Afterlife

The idea of an afterlife was an important part of Egyptian religion in the Middle and New Kingdoms. Many people believed that after death, the soul had the chance to become immortal. It could live forever in the Field of Reeds, the kingdom of the dead. The Field of Reeds was like an ideal version of Egypt. The Nile floods there were always the right level. Grain in the Field of Reeds grew twice as tall as in the Egypt of ordinary life.

Unfortunately, to reach the Field of Reeds, the soul—called the *ba*—had to pass a series of tests. During this journey the *ba* was usually shown as a bird with a human head.

First, the soul had to cross the Lake of Dawn to the Winding Water. A surly ferryman sailed a magical boat across the lake. Before he would give a *ba* passage, the *ba* must name the ferryman and every part of his boat.

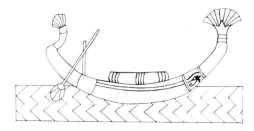

The underworld was divided into 12 hells. They corresponded to the 12 hours of the night. The *ba* had to enter and cross each of these 12 realms. The way to each realm was barred by a gate and guarded by three gods. The soul must name the gate and each of the three gods that guarded it. Only then could the soul go into that realm.

Each realm contained different dangers. In one, the *ba* must pass a boiling lake. Another contained a lake of fire. One realm was the home of the terrible serpent Apophis. In another, the *ba* must pass a snake that spat poison.

If the soul made it past all these dangers, it arrived at the doorway of Osiris' throne room, the Hall of the Two Truths. Before entering, the *ba* had to say the names of every part of the doorway.

Inside the Hall of the Two Truths, Thoth, the god of wisdom, met the *ba*. Thoth brought the soul to face the 42 judges of the underworld. Here the *ba* must greet each of the judges by name. It must swear that it had not committed any of the sins that judge punished.

If the *ba* passed this test, too, it came to the final test. Anubis, the guardian of the dead, stood by a balance scale in the center of the hall. A feather lay in one pan of the scales. This was the symbol of *ma'at*, the principle of truth and justice. Thoth stood by, ready to record the result of the test. Behind Thoth stood the monster Ammit, the devourer. Ammit had the head of a crocodile, the body of a lion, and the hind quarters of a hippopotamus.

(continued)

The Game of the Afterlife *(continued)*

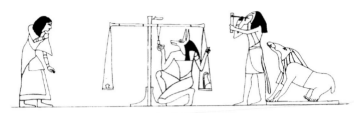

As the *ba* stood by the scales, Anubis took the *ba*'s heart and placed it in the other pan of the scales. If the heart was pure and free of sin, the heart and the feather balanced. Then the god Horus led the *ba* to the throne of Osiris. Here the *ba* became an *akh*, a blessed soul. It was free to live forever in the Field of Reeds.

However, if the heart of the *ba* was heavy with sin, it weighed down that side of the scales. Then the *ba* must suffer a second, eternal death. It was devoured by the monster Ammit.

 As you read through the steps of this journey, you will see that there were many places at which the *ba* could go wrong. The soul might never make it as far as the Hall of the Two Truths to face the test of ma'at.

Imagine a board game based on the *ba*'s journey through the underworld. A lucky card, a successful throw of the dice, could take it safely past obstacles. An unlucky move could destroy it forever.

Work in your group to develop a game called Journey to the Afterlife. The game should begin at the Lake of Dawn. It must include at least 10 stages on the journey, in the correct order, but it can include as many more as you wish. You could choose a format like Monopoly where players go around the board, facing risks and gaining rewards as they go. You could develop a maze, where some paths are dead ends. You could set it up like Snakes and Ladders, where one square leads the player up several rows and another sends the player down. Each player might start off with cards that can help it pass dangers. Players might be able to use the treasures of the tomb to bribe their way through.

Decide on a format for your game, and agree on the rules for playing it. Remember, you need to include at least 10 events from the *ba*'s journey, starting at the Lake of Dawn and ending in the Hall of the Two Truths.

Now create the game itself. Include a board and any other material, like cards or treasure, needed to play the game. If you wish, you can make small *ba* figures—birds with human heads—as your playing pieces. As much as possible, use Egyptian designs to decorate your game. Write out the rules of the game as clearly as you can.

When all groups have completed their games, follow your teacher's directions to try one another's games.

Glossary

Abydos	Chief site of Osiris worship; contains royal tombs of the First and Second Dynasties. Mystery plays reenacting the myth of Osiris were held here for centuries.
amulet	Charm or piece of jewelry worn as protection against evil, placed in mummy wrappings.
ankh	The sign of life.
Anubis	The god who prepared the deceased for the journey to the Afterlife and weighed the soul against the feather of ma'at in the Hall of the Two Truths.
***atef* crown**	Crown worn by Osiris.
ba	A name for the soul, often shown as a bird with a human head.
bartering	System of trade where money is not used. Goods are exchanged for other goods of the same value.
B.C.E.	Abbreviation for Before the Common Era.
Black Land	Fertile land in the valley and delta of the Nile River, called *kemet* by the ancient Egyptians.
Book of the Dead	Texts containing spells and charms placed in the tomb to help a dead person's soul through the dangers of the underworld. Two hundred different spells were used in all, but no one text uses all two hundred.
cartouche	Oval in which the name of the pharaoh was written.
crook	Stick with curved top used by a shepherd with sheep. Carried by god or pharaoh to symbolize kingship, it shows that the king cared for his people as a shepherd cared for his sheep.
cult	Worship of a particular god.
deben	Metal ring used by traders to measure weight. One deben weighed about 4 oz (90 g).
delta	The marshy area in northern Egypt where the Nile flows into the Mediterranean. The delta lands of ancient Egypt were rich and fertile, and many wild animals and birds lived there.
demotic script	Later development of hieratic script, even more removed from hieroglyphics than hieratic. From 700 B.C.E. on, used for administration and business.
determinative	Hieroglyph symbol that indicated the general area of meaning of a word. Determinatives were not pronounced.
djed pillar	Sign of stability and peace.
Duat	The Underworld, which the ba had to pass through to gain eternal life.

dynasty	Succession of rulers belonging to related families. The history of ancient Egypt included 31 dynasties.
embalmer	In ancient Egypt, a person who treated a dead body with salt, spices, oil to keep it from decaying.
Field of Reeds	Name for the kingdom of Osiris, the land of the dead.
flail	Tool consisting of a heavy club, attached to a long handle with a hinge, used to separate grain from chaff. Carried by god or pharaoh to symbolize kingship, fertility of the land.
fulcrum	Balance point of a lever.
Geb	God of the earth.
gum arabic	Gum from trees, used as paint fixative.
hieratic script	Simplified, cursive version of hieroglyphics, used for most papyri.
hieroglyphics	Picture writing of ancient Egypt. Later two derivative scripts, hieratic and demotic, were developed.
Horus	The son of Osiris, usually shown with the head of a falcon.
irrigation	A system of ditches and canals used to move water from a river or lake into the fields.
Isis	Sister-wife of Osiris, mother of Horus.
ka	Life force of a person, born at the same time, which accompanied the person through life. It could live on after the person's death if it was provided with food and an image of the person to use as a resting place.
Kingdom	In Egyptian history, a period of time. Old Kingdom: 2886–2181 B.C.E.; Middle Kingdom: 1991–1786 B.C.E.; New Kingdom: 1568–1085 B.C.E.
kohl	Black eye cosmetic worn by both men and women.
Ma'at	Egyptian goddess of justice, truth, world order. Symbolized by an ostrich feather.
malachite	Copper ore, crushed and used as cosmetic for eyes, pigment for paint.
mummification	Process of drying and embalming that preserves dead body of a person or animal.
mummy	Embalmed body, wrapped in linen bands.
mystery play	Play based on religious theme.
natron	Natural salt from the desert that absorbs water, used in the mummification process.
Nephthys	Sister of Isis, with whom she always appears; sister-wife of Seth, Osiris' brother and murderer.
Nut	Goddess of the sky, mother of Osiris, Seth, Nephthys.

Osiris	God of grain, rebirth, and resurrection. Usually shown as a mummy with green skin, wearing the crown of the two Egypts and carrying the flail and the crook of kingship.
papyrus	Reed used for many purposes in ancient Egypt. Its pith was used to make a writing material, also called papyrus. The reeds were used for such varied products as boats, mats, ropes, sandals, and baskets.
Pharaoh	Ruler of ancient Egypt. Name comes from Egyptian word *per-ao*, "Great House," which referred to the palace where the ruler lived.
pigment	Powder mixed with a liquid to make ink or paint.
Red Land	Barren desert lands beyond the Nile River valley and delta. The ancient Egyptians called it *deshret*.
relief	Shallow carving on stone or wood, where parts of the image stood out from the background.
ritual	Procedure for religious ceremony.
scarab	Dung beetle. This beetle lays its eggs in animal dung, then forms the dung into a ball and rolls it around with its pincers until the eggs hatch. Because the eggs seemed to hatch out of nothing, the Egyptians used the beetle as the symbol of regeneration and new life. The scarab was often used as a protective amulet.
scribe	Person trained to read and write. Most scribes worked for the government, recording court cases, assessing and collecting taxes, etc.
senet	Game played by Egyptians with a board and counters. It had lucky and unlucky squares, and was probably similar to the modern game of checkers.
Seth	God of chaos, the desert, storm, war. Brother and murderer of Osiris.
shabti/ushabti	"Answerer," small figure designed to work in the Field of Reeds in place of the deceased. Usually shown in the shape of a mummy.
shaduf	Irrigation device consisting of a long pole with a bucket at one end, and a counterweight at the other, fixed to an upright. It was used to move water from the Nile to canals running through the fields.
silt	Fertile mud carried by the flooding Nile, left on the fields after the flood receded.
sistrum	Musical instrument.
Thoth	God of wisdom and of the moon, taught people to read, write, use numbers. Often shown with the head of an ibis or a baboon.
uraeus	Sacred serpent shown on headdress of rulers and gods.

wedjat eye   Amulet based on eye of Horus; symbol of renewal of life, protected carrier from the unexpected.

vizier   The highest official in Egyptian government, second only to the pharaoh in importance.

Resources

Egyptian Art

http://www.directnet.com/history/Institute of Egyptian Art and Architecture.

http://www.cc.emory.edu/CARLOS/egypt.cal.html M.C. Carlos Museum permanent collection of Egyptian art.

Aldred, Cyril. *Egyptian Art in the Days of the Pharaohs 3100–320 B.C.* New York: Thames and Hudson, 1985.

Glubok, Shirley. *The Art of Egypt Under the Pharaohs.* New York: Macmillan Publishing Company Inc., 1980.

General World Wide Web Sites

http://csc.sctboces.org/elmira/coburn/egypt.htm Offers brief text and images on a variety of subjects including papyrus, geography, and Egyptian gods.

http://pages.prodigy.com/guardian/egypt.htm Provides links to many Egypt and Egyptology resources on the WWW.

http://www.sirius.com/~reeder/links.html Another page featuring a number of links to sites relating to Egypt.

http://scrtec.org/track/tracks/f00025.html Information and activities geared to students.

http://www.sptimes.com/Egypt/Quiz/Default.html "The Pharaoh's Challenge," a multiple-choice quiz that includes serious and frivolous information.

http://www.rom.on.ca/eyouths/egyptqiz.htm The Royal Ontario Museum site features a visual quiz showing some common Egyptian items.

General History of Egypt

Defrates, Joanna. *What Do We Know About the Egyptians?* New York: Peter Bedrick Books, 1991.

Harris, Geraldine. *Cultural Atlas for Young People: Ancient Egypt.* New York: Facts on File, 1990.

MacDonald, Fiona. *Insights: Ancient Egyptians.* New York: Barron's, 1993.

Morley, Jacqueline, Mark Bergin, and John James. *Inside Story: An Egyptian Pyramid.* New York: Peter Bedrick Books, 1991.

Steedman, Scott. *Pockets: Ancient Egypt.* New York: Dorling Kindersley, 1995. This plentifully illustrated little book organizes information by topics for easy use.

Egyptian Figure Drawing

Aldred, Cyril. *Egyptian Art in the Days of the Pharaohs 3100–320 B.C.* New York: Thames and Hudson, 1985.

Glubok, Shirley. *The Art of Egypt Under the Pharaohs.* New York: Macmillan Publishing Company Inc., 1980.

Sibbett, Ed, Jr. *Ancient Egyptian Design Coloring Book.* New York: Dover Publications Inc., 1978.

Hieroglyphics

http://www.netvision.be/egyptologicale_les1.htm Step-by-step lessons on reading hieroglyphics.

http://www2.torstar.com/rom/egypt/egypt.html Interactive site translates from English letters to hieroglyphics and back.

www2.torstar.com/rom/egypt Describes how the hieroglyphic system worked.

Katan, Norma Jean, with Barbara Mintz. *Hieroglyphs: The Writing of Ancient Egypt*. New York: Atheneum, 1981. An accessible approach to hieroglyphics.

Rossini, Stéphane. *Egyptian Hieroglyphics: How to Read and Write Them*. New York: Dover Publications Inc., 1989.

Egyptian Math

http://eyelid.ukonline.co.uk/ancient/numbers.htm Site includes information about Egyptian numbers, some word problems set in Egypt, and using hieroglyphic numbers.

Lumpkin, Beatrice, and Dorothy Strong. *Multicultural Science and Math Connections: Middle School Projects and Activities*. Portland, ME: J. Weston Walch, Publisher, 1995.

Woods, Geraldine. *Science in Ancient Egypt*. New York: Franklin Watts, 1988.

Zaslavsky, Claudia. *Multicultural Mathematics: Interdisciplinary Cooperative-Learning Activities*. Portland, ME: J. Weston Walch, Publisher, 1993.

Medicine and Magic

Mayer, Josephine, and Tom Prideaux. *Never to Die: The Egyptians in Their Own Words*. New York: The Viking Press, 1938.

Wilkinson, Richard H. *Symbol and Magic in Egyptian Art*. London: Thames and Hudson, 1994.

The Eloquent Peasant

Harris, Geraldine. *Gods & Pharaohs from Egyptian Mythology*. New York: Peter Bedrick Books, 1992.

Mayer, Josephine, and Tom Prideaux. *Never to Die: The Egyptians in Their Own Words*. New York: The Viking Press, 1938.

Simpson, William Kelly, ed. *The Literature of Ancient Egypt: An Anthology of Stories, Instructions, and Poetry*. New Haven and London: Yale University Press, 1972.

Religion: Hundreds of Gods

David, A.R. *The Ancient Egyptians: Religious Beliefs and Practices*. London and New York: Routledge and Kegan Paul, 1982, reprinted 1986.

Harris, Geraldine. *Gods & Pharaohs from Egyptian Mythology*. New York: Peter Bedrick Books, 1992.

Lurker, Manfred. *The Gods and Symbols of Ancient Egypt: An Illustrated Dictionary*. London: Thames and Hudson, 1980.

Quirke, Stephen. *Ancient Egyptian Religion*. New York: Dover, 1995, 1992.

Drama: The Festival of Osiris

Harris, Geraldine. *Gods & Pharaohs from Egyptian Mythology.* New York: Peter Bedrick Books, 1992.

Mayer, Josephine, and Tom Prideaux. *Never to Die: The Egyptians in Their Own Words.* New York: The Viking Press, 1938.

McDermot, Gerald. *The Voyage of Osiris: A Myth of Ancient Egypt.* New York: Windmill Books, 1977.

Games of Ancient Egypt

http://www.teleport.com/~ddonahue/senet.html Downloadable shareware version of senet reconstruction.

http://www.gamecabinet.com/history/Senet.html A reconstruction of the rules for playing senet.

Arnold, Arnold. *The World Book of Children's Games.* New York: World Publishing, 1972. Includes rules for the finger game, Nine Men's Morris, and alquerque, another game played in ancient Egypt. It also offers a reconstruction of the rules for playing senet, probably the most popular board game in ancient Egypt.

Making a Mummy

Andrews, Carol. *Egyptian Mummies.* Cambridge, MA: Harvard University Press (British Museum Series), 1984.

Glubok, Shirley, and Alfred Tamaria. *The Mummy of Ramose: The Life and Death of an Ancient Egyptian Nobleman.* New York: Harper and Row, 1978.

Pace, Mildred Mastin. *Wrapped for Eternity: The Story of the Egyptian Mummy.* New York: McGraw-Hill Book Company, 1974.

Putnam, James. *Mummy.* New York: A.A. Knopf, 1993.

The Game of the Afterlife

Glubok, Shirley, and Alfred Tamaria. *The Mummy of Ramose: The Life and Death of an Ancient Egyptian Nobleman.* New York: Harper and Row, 1978.

Lattimore, Deborah Nourse. *The Winged Cat: A Tale of Ancient Egypt.* New York: HarperCollins Publishers, 1992. A picture book that shows crossing the underworld to the Hall of the Two Truths.